The Lost Years

The Lost Years

Tranquillisers and after—
the effect minor tranquillisers
can have on our life
and our families

Joan Jerome
with
Lindi Bilgorri

VIRGIN

First published in Great Britain in 1991 by
Virgin Books
an imprint of Virgin Publishing
338 Ladbroke Grove
London W10 5AH

British Library Cataloguing in Publication Data
Jerome, Joan–
    The lost years: tranquillisers and after: the effect
    minor tranquillisers can have on our life and our
    families.
    1. Tranquillisers. Addiction
    I. Title   II. Bilgorri, Lindi
    362.299

    ISBN 1–85227–373–9

Designed by Mick Keates

Typeset by Phoenix Photosetting, Chatham, Kent
Printed and bound in Great Britain by
Mackays of Chatham PLC, Chatham, Kent

With thanks to my now grown-up children Maira, Judy, Yatta and Luke for tolerating me when I wasn't the mother I should have been.

Joan Jerome

Joan Jerome is currently running a private, independent service for those suffering from tranquilliser dependence. This service can deal only with written enquiries.

For further details, please send a stamped, self-addressed envelope to:

TRANXCALL
PO Box 440
Harrow
Middlesex

CONTENTS

FOREWORD
by Nick Ross

Back in 1979 I made a film about a junkie. I was working for the BBC and was revisiting a favourite subject for press and television. Drug abuse had been increasing since the 1960s, and fears were mounting that Britain was falling victim to the truly epic drug-related problems of the United States.

The programme didn't turn out quite as we expected; indeed the problem we discovered was very different from the popular and established view of drug addiction. Firstly, heroin was not the major issue—let alone cocaine. Only a tiny minority of young people who used drugs for recreation could get their hands on any of the classic opiates. Instead they turned to almost anything, but notably to barbiturates, a group of tranquillising drugs whose name was aptly shortened in street language simply to 'barbs'. Secondly, illicit drug abuse did not appear to me to be as great or damaging an issue as the much more acceptable, but widespread, injury caused by the use of alcohol and tobacco. Thirdly, drug *abuse* was overshadowed by a problem I'd not heard much about before: drug dependency induced by doctors.

Heroin, of course, was once a widely prescribed medicine regarded as safe, reliable and non-addictive. Only after many years did its habit-forming properties become a real source of concern, and eventually barbiturates were ushered in as a safe alternative. At the time we were making our film, barbs were being recognised as habit-forming too. A new group of wonder-pharmaceuticals was being used instead: benzodiazapines, such as Valium. These in turn were thought to be safe and non-addictive, but perhaps the very process of tranquillising people for months on end, by means of whatever drug, creates changes in the person's make-up that opens up the likelihood of drug dependency.

Be that as it may, doctors have for years been dishing out prescriptions for tranquillising drugs. 'Tranx', as they are often known, are an effective treatment for many conditions, including psychological trauma; and if patients returned and asked for more there seemed no harm in it. Moreover, tranquillisers had a singular property not shared effectively with any other treatment known to medicine: they could get problem patients, those with no obvious signs of injury or illness, out of the surgery quickly and with mutual contentment. GPs sometimes speak of 'heart-sink' patients—those who make the doctor's heart sink when they walk in through the door. Tranquillisers disposed of most of them with great dispatch.

The result has been that millions of people across the world have become dependent on repeat prescriptions of these mood-changing drugs. To put it bluntly, these people are medically induced junkies. The pills may keep them stable, but they also trap them. Long-term use of tranquillisers tends to rob people of part of their lives.

One further thing our film research made plain was equally uncomfortable. Most drug rehabilitation centres simply did not seem to work, and in any case tended to concentrate on 'recreational' drug addicts. The main problem with drug *abusers* (those who take 'street drugs' and at first used them for fun) is that they rarely *want* to be drug-free. Success can only follow an absolute determination to change one's style of life for good.

However, the great majority of drug-dependent people whom we came across were *users* not abusers—people who took no pleasure from their dependency and often wanted to be free of it—and in theory help for these people should be much more successful. We did indeed stumble on one form of treatment which appeared to be remarkably effective. It relied on no costly or sophisticated form of living-in or long-term psychoanalysis, and avoided the desperate narrow-mindedness that can dog the drug rehabilitation world. It consisted of counselling by *ex-users*, people who *had* been dependent on tranx but had found a way to freedom.

It sounds remarkably simple, and it was; moreover, independent assessment and follow-up found it to be remarkably successful. Sensibly enough, the organisation was known first as TRANX, later as TRANX (UK). Its founder was a former user, Joan Jerome, the co-author of this book, and I commend it to you.

Nick Ross is a journalist and broadcaster. He presents Call Nick Ross *on Radio 4 and* Crimewatch UK *on BBC1, and produced a major BBC TV documentary on drug use called* The Fix. *In 1985 he also co-presented (with Esther Rantzen)* Drugwatch *on BBC1, which launched the 'Just Say No' campaign.*

ACKNOWLEDGEMENTS

Firstly, Joan wishes to thank Dr David Marjot for showing her the way to recovery.

We are very grateful for the invaluable information and support given by Dr Heather Ashton, Dr R. Bhatt, Dr B. Ettore, Jean Kilshaw, Dr David Marjot, Professor M. Lader, Paul Newton-Syms, Dr Mark Tattersall, Ulla Tönne and the British Medical Library.

Our thanks also to Monica Burton, psychotherapist and hypnotherapist, for her kind permission to include her relaxation technique on pp. 167–8. (Monica Burton can be contacted by telephone on 081–422 0402).

We would also like to express our appreciation to all the clients and their families who had the courage to talk openly and sometimes painfully about themselves. In return for their trust in revealing their innermost thoughts to us, we have respected their privacy and given them all pseudonyms. Thus their emotions are known to all, but they remain anonymous.

For ease of writing we have generally used the pronoun 'she' when referring to sufferers, but of course the facts apply equally to men and women. Likewise, we have used the pronoun 'he' when referring to doctors in general, but again these statements refer equally to male and female doctors.

The world of medicine is continually changing, but as far as we are aware all the facts are correct at the time of writing.

Our gratitude also goes to Frankie Tredler and the staff of TRANX (UK), and especially to Blanche for all the toing and froing of the manuscript.

Of course, the book could not have happened without the guidance of our agent, Anne Dewe, and Gill Gibbins, our editor at Virgin.

And Lindi wishes to give a very special thank-you to her husband Brian and their two children Chloe and Guy who supported and encouraged her during the writing of the book.

INTRODUCTION

BENZODIAZEPINES – MY VIEW OF THE STORY SO FAR

'The difference between man and animal is that man takes drugs.'
William Osler

Eureka! Here were pills reported to wipe away our stress, anxiety and insomnia without any harmful effects. Benzodiazepines—'wonder pills' or 'happy pills', as they were nicknamed. We swallowed them in our millions, seduced by the temptation of a trouble-free life. But how gullible we all were! And for our naivety, we endured pain and suffering before the real truth came out more than twenty years after their birth.

THE 1960s

The benzodiazepine story starts just before the sixties in 1957, when Dr Leo Sternbach discovered a drug of an entirely new chemical class at the Roche Nutley Laboratories in the United States. It caused much excitement in the pharmaceutical and medical professions because it was found to have a powerful taming effect on wild animals. The animals could be petted, and yet were still lively and alert. Roche were so excited with this discovery that they carried out extensive clinical trials for two years (1958–60) involving 16,000 people. The results of the trials gave benzodiazepines a completely clean bill of health. The drug caused few side-effects, except slight drowsiness and lack of co-ordination, but its researchers had no reason to believe it was addictive, and Roche stated: 'The drug has a wide margin of safety.' It was put on the market under the name of chlordiazepoxide or Librium.[1]

For doctors, it must truly have seemed a 'wonder drug'. They could prescribe it for a variety of ailments. It could be given to the patient who was upset over a broken marriage and to the one who had backache. It could be used by the patient who suffered from sleeplessness and also by the one with personal worries. It was given as a 'pre-med' and as an anti-convulsant. But doctors didn't delight in the drug just because it could be used for so many conditions; after all, other sedatives such as barbiturates had been used equally widely for many years. What made benzodiazepines special was that it was thought to be almost impossible for an adult to commit suicide by taking them on their own. A handful of tablets taken in overdose merely gave the patient a long sleep. In fact, doctors joked, the only way to overdose an experimental guinea-pig to death with benzo-diazepines was to bury it alive in tablets![2]

Of course, because Librium quickly became one of the most popular drugs, everyone wanted to get in on its success. Various pharmaceutical companies did more research to find better versions of the existing compounds, or to find drugs of a similar type but with different effects. So then a string of benzodiazepines from different manufacturers came on the market, such as diazepam (Valium), nitrazepam (Mogadon) and oxazepam (Serenid-D, later replaced by Oxanid). Some were pure tranquillisers, some were sleeping pills or sedatives for minor surgical procedures, and others were to relieve certain forms of epilepsy. Valium was soon considered to be the best all-rounder. By the end of 1962 more than 21,000 patients had taken part in clinical trials involving Valium.

But to understand the success story of benzodiazepines we have to look further afield than the doctor's surgery and the pharmaceutical company's laboratory. We have to look at the social climate of the time. Librium came in with the 'swinging sixties' and the permissive society. It was a time of affluence, change and freedom, when any-thing seemed possible. The mini-skirt arrived and became shorter and shorter; the first supermarkets were seen on the high street; housewives could buy their first frozen foods and TV dinners; more people had cars; the first package holidays were introduced; the hippy culture came in, with the slogan 'make love not war'. It was a decade when people weren't prepared to put up with hardship—they felt they didn't have to any more. They wanted instant satisfaction: as benzodiazepines work quickly, the drug gave instant relief from their problems.

The sixties was also a time when the drug-taking ethic was more fashionable. We became a nation that seemed to be, on reflection, pill-popping mad, with both legal and illegal drugs. The hippies and pop groups were renowned for taking illegal drugs, such as marijuana and cocaine. Housewives, who may well have been against such drug abuse, took tranquillisers. These two sections of society saw each other as being at opposite poles, with different views and outlooks, but they were, in fact, very similar in one respect—they took their drugs to escape.

As pills were so widely accepted by society, the patient as well as the doctor relied on benzodiazepines to cure all forms of anxiety, no matter how minor. When we entered the doctor's surgery we expected to be given a bottle of tablets for treating our stress and anxiety; if we weren't, we felt cheated. Dr Peter Tyrer, now Senior Lecturer and Consultant Psychiatrist at St Charles Hospital, London, had just started in psychiatric practice in the mid-sixties. 'I was surprised', he says, 'that when I tried to avoid giving a drug to patients with anxiety, patients used to go out and say they hadn't been treated because the doctor just talked, he never gave any tablets.'

However, there were a few people in the medical profession who weren't as enthusiastic about benzodiazepines as the rest. In those early years, some doctors were already finding that there were in fact disturbing side-effects of drowsiness, lack of co-ordination, dizziness, aggression and loss of weight.[3] However, out of all the clinical trials done at the time, there was only one report of withdrawal symptoms in patients. But this finding had little significance because the dose taken was way above the recommended prescribing levels for a long period of time.[4]

So why weren't the side-effects and withdrawal symptoms which we know of today picked up in those early clinical trials—trials which could have saved millions of people from a life of misery? According to Arabella Melville and Colin Johnson, clinical trials are not always as truthful as we might expect them to be. They revealed in their book *Cured to Death*: 'If the data produced by one specialist are not quite what was hoped for, it is quite in order for the company to continue trials elsewhere until satisfactory results and testimonials are achieved. Negative results are very rarely published and indeed some clinicians tell of pressure to keep quiet about such data.' And a London GP, Dr Rhamesh Bhatt, says: 'Not all side-effects can be detected at clinical trials. Clinical trials are merely there to satisfy the Committee on Safety of Medicines (CSM). Only in the last ten years was the Post Marketing Surveillance (PMS) developed in order to do long-term follow-ups. The PMS was not done with benzodiazepines: had the PMS been around at the time, then the widespread use of benzodiazepines would have been prevented, as the long-term side-effects might have been detected then.'

One of the pharmaceutical manufacturers, Roche, states that although the PMS only came into being ten years ago, it and other drug companies continued their clinical trials throughout the sixties to monitor their marketed drugs—including benzodiazepines—but no convincing evidence was found of dependence or withdrawal. They also state that all clinical trials require approval from the Department of Health with the condition that all adverse reactions are reported, and that many clinical trials are carried out by independent investigators without any involvement from the manufacturer in question, other than supplying the trial drug.

So, if clinical trials are not totally reliable, should the doctor take more responsibility for detecting withdrawal symptoms, side-effects and dependence? After all, he is seeing the patient on a regular basis. He may even spot changes and symptoms in his patient. But Dr Bhatt says this is rather like putting the cart before the horse. 'If clinical trials did not indicate withdrawal symptoms,' he says, 'then how could the doctor be expected to indicate these whilst he was not expecting them nor looking for them?' As the doctor did not know about side-effects, withdrawal symptoms and dependence, he could have misinterpreted these signs in his patients as the original condition coming back. Withdrawal symptoms are, after all, very similar to severe anxiety symptoms.

THE 1970s

The seventies were the heyday of benzodiazdepines. By 1979, prescriptions for the drug in the United Kingdom had soared to more
than 30 million a year for a population of 55 million.[5] Doctors, like
their patients, were still in a dream about this drug's remarkable
powers. They still saw it as a cure for life's ills, with no risks
attached. In fact, doctors were positively encouraged at the beginning of the decade to change over from barbiturates to benzodiazepines, because of the latter's very high margin of safety. Malcolm
Lader, Professor of Clinical Psychopharmacology, Maudsley Hospital, London, wrote: 'The benzodiazepines are highly preferable to
the barbiturates because they are more effective and much safer.'[6]

Dependence still had not been detected sufficiently to cause alarm.
By 1978, a worldwide survey of dependence was published by Dr
John Marks, then Fellow and Director of Medical Studies at Cam-
bridge University, but until 1976 managing director at Roche
Laboratories. He found that in the sixteen-year period from 1961 to
1977, only 500 cases of dependence worldwide were reported, and
just 28 cases in the United Kingdom.[7] This translated to a one-in-a-
million risk. He stated: 'Benzodiazepines can produce psychological
and physical dependence if given in excessive doses, over a pro-
longed period and particularly to patients with unstable personali-
ties.' But he concluded: 'The dependence risk factor is . . . so low
that no extension of controls is necessary.'[8]

But at that time, when most doctors saw benzodiazepine dependence as negligible and occurring only with 'excessive' doses, I was
taking a normal therapeutic dose and I was hooked, along with
thousands of other users. Alas, no one knew, no one realised. We
simply did not appear in the statistics of those dependent on benzodiazepines!

In the late seventies I had been on benzodiazepines for nearly ten
years. My dose, which had started out at 5mg of Valium, had risen to
15–20mg a day. I was also taking other drugs, for what I later
discovered were the side-effects of the benzodiazepines. I was a
walking zombie. I was becoming aggressive and irritable with my
four children. When I went to bed I couldn't sleep, even though I was
taking hypnotics (sleeping pills) hourly throughout the night. Deep

down, I knew the pills were the cause of my problems. I knew I shouldn't take the tablets. But I couldn't help it because I was trapped—I was addicted. Of course, my doctor did not show concern over the amount of pills I was taking; in fact, she referred to benzodiazepines as 'Smarties', and told me how safe and non-addictive they were. She didn't want to hear my pleas for help. Her surgery was so busy, she didn't have time to deal with my worries and fears of addiction.

THE 1980s

In 1980 the report of the Committee on Review of Medicines cast doubt on these supposed 'wonder' drugs. It showed that, among other things, benzodiazepines were not suitable for treating tension headaches, menstruation and depression problems. (Although the manufacturers never indicated benzodiazepines for the treatment of depression, some doctors do prescribe them for this purpose.) The report also showed that benzodiazepines could have adverse reactions in the elderly. They lost their sleep-promoting properties when taken for a long period of time. They caused withdrawal symptoms when stopped abruptly. The committee suggested that as a sleeping pill (hypnotic) they should only be taken for three to fourteen days, and as a tranquilliser for up to four months. But regarding dependence the report stated: 'the true addiction potential of benzodiazepines was low'.[9] However, the report caused enough of a stir for new guidelines to be sent to 30,000 doctors across the UK in order to encourage them to change their prescribing habits.

A year later, Professor Malcolm Lader found in his study that patients on a therapeutic dose of benzodiazepines were suffering withdrawal symptoms, and that these symptoms were not the same as the original anxiety symptoms, as previously believed. He concluded his report in the *British Medical Journal* by saying: 'Our findings . . . show that patients taking benzodiazepines in therapeutic doses risk developing some form of dependence . . . detecting withdrawal symptoms in patients taking normal therapeutic doses increases the urgency of the problem and argues against regular daily medication for chronic anxiety. Many thousands of patients may be at risk, as some two per cent or so of the adult population take benzo-diazepines chronically.'[10]

In the early eighties, I had also made a few discoveries myself. I was learning how hard, painful and protracted a process it was to come off my drugs. In 1982 I was the first pure tranquilliser-user to be admitted into the Drug Dependency Unit of St Bernard's Hospital, London, under Dr David Marjot. There, among heroin addicts and alcoholics, I slowly weaned myself off my 'habit' in the security of the hospital surroundings.

I also learnt that tranquilliser addicts were alone and, unlike the alcoholic and the hard-drug user, had no on-going help or guidance. So by the end of that year, while still in recovery from my addiction, I began to set up TRANX, the world's pilot self-help organisation for minor tranquilliser addicts. My full story can be read in Part Six.

Meanwhile, further studies were done by various doctors, stripping benzodiazepines of their no-risk status. Indeed, the medical world was starting to find out that they were just as addictive and as hard to come off as other sedatives, if not more so. In fact, in 1982 the Martindale (the doctors' encyclopedia) actually warned that dependence was liable to occur in susceptible patients. Then the theory that dependence could only happen after a pro-longed period was finally quashed when Professor Malcolm Lader reported that withdrawal symptoms occurred after treatment for as little as four to six weeks.

In April 1985 some benzodiazepines were removed from the NHS list of prescribable branded medicines. Roche UK phar-maceutical sales were reduced by 40 per cent. During this period the company made 200 redundancies at its factory in Welwyn Garden City.[11]

But it wasn't until 1988 that doctors finally had a list of recom-mendations based on previous studies, suggesting that addiction could also occur on a low therapeutic dose—something I had been saying for over five years. This was revealed in the Committee on Safety of Medicines report in the January of that year, turning the wonder drug of the sixties into the unfashionable drug of the eighties and nineties.

The report recommended that the use of benzodiazepines should be limited in the following ways:

'1. Benzodiazepines are indicated for the short-term relief (two to four weeks only) of anxiety that is severe, disabling or subjecting the individual to unacceptable distress, occurring alone or in association with insomnia or short-term psychosomatic organic or psychotic illness.

2. The use of benzodiazepines to treat short-term "mild" anxiety is inappropriate and unsuitable.

3. Benzodiazepines should be used to treat insomnia only when it is severe, disabling, or subjecting the individual to extreme distress.'

The report recommended the correct dosage:

'1. The lowest dose which can control the symptoms should be used. It should not be continued beyond four weeks.

2. Long-term chronic use is not recommended.

3. Treatment should always be tapered off gradually.

4. Patients who have taken benzodiazepines for a long time may require a longer period during which doses are reduced.

5. When a benzodiazepine is used as a hypnotic, treatment should, if possible, be intermittent.'

It then set forward a list of precautions:

'1. Benzodiazepines should not be used alone to treat depression or anxiety associated with depression. Suicide may be precipitated in such patients.

2. They should not be used for phobic or obsessional states.

3. They should not be used for the treatment of chronic psychosis.

4. In cases of loss or bereavement, psychological adjustment may be inhibited by benzodiazepines.

5. Disinhibiting effects may be manifested in various ways. Suicide may be precipitated in patients who are depressed, and aggressive behaviour towards self and others may be precipitated. Extreme

caution should therefore be used in prescribing benzodiazepines in patients with personality disorders.'

At last the medical profession had the facts. But for the tranquilliser addicts it came over twenty years too late. Doctors and the pharmaceutical industry can apologetically say: sorry, we did do trials to find out about the drug which continuously proved it to be safe, and armed with that evidence we thought we were giving the best possible treatment. But 'sorry' isn't enough for the tranquilliser user. 'Sorry' isn't going to give back the lost years spent taking the drug, and 'sorry' isn't going to stop the pain in withdrawal. 'Sorry' isn't going to bring back husbands and children who left us because of our addiction. 'Sorry' isn't enough. But what else can they say?

PART ONE

PRESCRIPTION

I

FALLING INTO THE TRAP

'I took tranquillisers to take away the pain, but they only gave me grief.'

Anyone can get hooked on tranquillisers. No one is immune. It isn't a pill only taken by the neurotic or weak-minded—the little house-wife who can't cope. Far from it: in fact, very strong-minded, effi-cient and highly respected men and women have become addicted to benzodiazepines.

But why are we all so vulnerable? Quite simply, it's the lives we lead. Every day demands, disasters, dramas, and expectations are thrown at us like the balls that are hurled at a coconut shy. When we are knocked and feel ourselves falling, we grab for something to keep us steady. Unfortunately, in many cases, that something ends up being tranquillisers.

Just everyday events can cause anxiety: pressure of work, un-employment, a newborn baby, the demands of young children, exam nerves, flying, noisy neighbours, divorce, the death of a loved one, insomnia, an accident or an unhappy relationship. In the USA, Dr R. H. Rahe found 43 life pressures which can cause stress. He put them in a table, taking death of a spouse as the most traumatic, with other pressures following in order of decreasing severity. Below is a list of some of the life events which can affect us.[12]

A little bit of stress or anxiety isn't bad for us—it gets our adre-naline going. Dr Temple, Senior Vice President, Central Nervous System Research, Pharmaceutical Research and Development

Division, Bristol-Myers Squibb Co. Ltd, USA, explains: 'Normal or situational anxiety is good. It's what drives us through life, it's what keeps us out of trouble and it shouldn't be treated. And I think when we do treat an anxiety when it relates to our problems in our lives, we are asking for big trouble.' However, we can, of course, have too much anxiety. Dr Rahe suggests that when our score on his stress chart goes above 300, we may suffer a serious illness.

	Stress rating
Death of a spouse or partner	100
Divorce	73
Marital separation	65
Personal injury or illness	53
Loss of job	47
Pregnancy	40
Sexual problems	39
Taking on a large mortgage	31
Change in residence	20
Vacation	13

Whatever the reason for our anxiety, today's society expects us to grin and bear it. We have to put on a stiff upper lip and not show our emotions or anger. We have to be what society likes us to be—calm, collected and able to cope. So what happens to our anxiety? We try to bury it. We subdue these painful emotions, so that we can appear to be acting normally. But, of course, our emotions can't be stifled—instead they corrode and fester inside us until we can't take it any longer and we snap. That's when we reach out for tranquillisers.

Just as society demands a lot from us, so we expect a lot from society. We don't want problems. We want our worries to vanish. Who hasn't said, 'I wish this problem would just go away'? And, unfortunately, tranquillisers do appear to magic the problem away—they work very quickly. After taking our first dose of benzodiazepines we may feel confident and able to cope, or it may be our first night's sleep in months. But although we *appear* to feel better, the problem is still there: it hasn't gone away, it's just been buried even deeper.

What's really needed is for people to *talk* about their problems. That's easy to say, but the way western society is structured, it is very hard to do. You may ask, who shall I talk to? I have no-one to be my listening ear—my mother lives miles away, my sister is abroad, my best friend's a gossip or won't understand, my husband won't listen, and anyway they will all think I'm just trouble.

It isn't easy. Unfortunately, for many people there is no longer that wonderful network of parents, aunts, sisters and brothers—the extended family—living nearby, that you could go to for advice or support, who you could share your problems with over a cup of tea. Nor is professional help easy to find—often it's not even there, or there is a long waiting list. The UK is desperately short of counsellors, which is such a pity because so many addicts have said to me, 'if only I had someone who I could have talked to at the time, I wouldn't have ended up on pills.'

But it isn't only the structure of society which has stopped us from discussing our problems. In today's family set-up husbands, wives and children often don't talk to each other. Of course, they chat about day-to-day events, but root problems are rarely mentioned. Very few families know how each of the members feel about one another, and they don't know whether they are happy or sad. Sometimes, they get to a point where they are scared to reveal their true feelings because it would upset this fake balance. It would be a fly in the artificial ointment. So instead they pretend to themselves and to the outside world that they are happy, contented and successful.

The anxiety we experience can start at any time in our lives: it can even be something that began when we were a child. Maybe we are not aware that the problem could have stemmed from events in those early years. Whenever the anxiety first sets in, we are only punishing ourselves by not speaking up and not off-loading our fears. We are not being truthful to ourselves, so we allow the anxiety to gnaw away inside. Of course, the anxiety we experience is a very unpleasant emotion. As Professor Malcolm Lader says: 'If it wasn't unpleasant, we would not want treatment for it. It's all pervading, it's something which governs every action we do.'

But what brings us to the general practitioner's surgery? What makes us telephone for an appointment? Very few people go to the surgery to tell the doctor that they can't keep up with the pressure at work, or that they can't cope with the children, or that their marriage looks as if it's breaking up. People go to the doctor because of physical symptoms, but Professor Malcolm Lader believes that 15 per cent of the people who go to their GPs are actually suffering from anxiety.[13] Stress and anxiety manifest themselves in many physical ways, some of which are loss of appetite, insomnia, dizziness, fainting, impotence, migraine, diarrhoea, menstrual problems and nausea.[14] Many a doctor's cure for all these problems may be benzodiazepines.

DO WOMEN NEED TRANQUILLISERS MORE THEN MEN?

With 66 to 75 per cent[15] of benzodiazepine prescriptions being made out to women, it may seem on the surface that women do need the drug more than men. Some people have gone so far as to say that tranquillisers are a 'woman's drug'. But nothing can be further from the truth. Women are prescribed tranquillisers more often than men because the medical profession and society have different expectations of men and women.

We admire a man for being strong and determined. It's largely accepted that he drowns his sorrows in a pint of beer at the pub. But if a woman shouts and screams she's looked upon as hysterical. It isn't acceptable. If she's angry she is expected to suppress her feelings and keep them under control.

Doctors have led us to believe that it's not unusual for women to be neutoric and anxious. We readily accept people saying 'that woman's nervy' or 'she suffers with her nerves'. But those statements aren't often made about a man. Ask yourself this question: how many men do you know who suffer with their nerves, and how many women?

So women are easily labelled as nervous or anxious types. Unfortunately, women have accepted this label. Many women readily

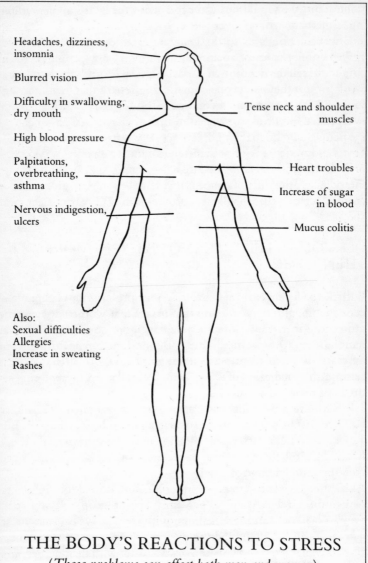

Headaches, dizziness, insomnia

Blurred vision

Difficulty in swallowing, dry mouth

High blood pressure

Palpitations, overbreathing, asthma

Nervous indigestion, ulcers

Tense neck and shoulder muscles

Heart troubles

Increase of sugar in blood

Mucus colitis

Also:
Sexual difficulties
Allergies
Increase in sweating
Rashes

THE BODY'S REACTIONS TO STRESS
(These problems can affect both men and women)

believe that they are a 'nervy' person. They believe it's in their make-up, and put the blame onto their own shoulders, instead of finding out the root of the problem. Also, women go to their GP more often than men. Sometimes they don't go for themselves, but accompany a child or an elderly relative, and during that visit they might discuss their own problems with the doctor.

At TRANX we found that women between the ages of 34 and 65 were the most likely to be prescribed tranquillisers, and more often than not they were married. This could be for a number of varying reasons: women may find themselves at full stretch being a provider and mother; they may find themselves locked in an unhappy relationship; they may be given little emotional support when confronted by a life crisis—bereavement, miscarriage, stillbirth; and they are more affected by life cycles—a new baby or children leaving home.

But there is another reason why more women than men are prescribed tranquillisers. The birth of benzodiazepines came at about the same time as the birth of women's liberation. Women were burning their bras, asserting themselves and realising that there was more to life than marriage and children, and many doctors were quietening them down with tranquillisers, so that they no longer marched on demonstrations or tried to get a powerful job, but found themselves back at the kitchen sink. It seems society subconsciously finds it difficult to cope with assertive women—somehow it upsets the balance.

MEN AND TRANQUILLISERS

Although not as many men are prescribed benzodiazepines, they still make up between 30 and 40 per cent. This is quite a high proportion when you consider that tranquillisers are supposed to be a woman's drug. The reason why we are unaware that so many men take tranquillisers and sleeping pills is that they are more inclined to be secretive about their pill-taking habits than women.

As with women, they fall into the tranquilliser trap because of the demands of society. Generally it is the pressure of work and financial worries that leads to their anxiety and sleeplessness. And of course, if the marriage is unstable, they too can reach for the bottle of benzo-diazepines. But getting hooked on tranquillisers might not start with a psychological problem—it might be from a sports injury. For instance, the enthusiastic squash player might injure his back or ankle in a match. He goes to the doctor for something to relieve the pain and he may be sent home with benzodiazepines to act as a muscle relaxant and help him sleep.

THE ELDERLY AND TRANQUILLISERS

Maybe the largest group of people who take benzodiazepines are the elderly. Over one million elderly people in Britain take sleeping pills every night. They account for 70 per cent of the prescriptions made out for benzodiazepines, which are generally hypnotics.[16] The reasons for them not being able to sleep can be pain, discomfort, loneliness and worry.

But possibly the most worrying aspect is what happens when the elderly are taken into care. One study has found that 42 per cent of the elderly in residential homes have received drugs without proper monitoring. And even more disturbing is that some (20 per cent) have been admitted into psycho-geriatric units because of the adverse effects of benzodiazepines. When these drugs were stopped the patients improved and were discharged.[17]

WHAT ARE BENZODIAZEPINES?

Benzodiazepines are minor tranquillisers. They are mood-altering or 'psychotropic' drugs, and one of the many types of psychotropic drugs your doctor can prescribe. In this book we are only discuss-ing benzodiazepine minor tranquillisers and sleeping pills, not major tranquillisers which are usually prescribed for major mental illnesses, such as schizophrenia. The well-known benzodiazepines are Valium (diazepam), Librium (chlordiazepoxide) and Ativan (lorazepam), but the pharmacist has over thirty different kinds of benzodiazepines on his shelves. They can either be prescribed under their chemical (generic) name or their brand name.

With so many tranquillisers and sleeping pills to choose from, it isn't surprising that patients are often confused about the type of pills they are taking. If the doctor changes their prescription, patients often think they are being given a different type of drug, when probably all that has changed is the name. The pill may still be one of the benzodiazepine group, at a higher or lower dosage. The doctor's choice of which benzodiazepine to prescribe will depend on what the patient's symptoms are. He can prescribe a tranquilliser or an anxiolytic for anxiety; or a hypnotic, more commonly known as a sleeping pill, for insomnia. Of course, not being able to sleep is often caused through anxiety and depression. Often people say to me 'I don't take tranquillisers, I just take a sleeping pill now and again'. Sleeping pills and tranquillisers are similar: they are both mood-altering drugs. You are living in a fool's paradise if you believe you're not 'on pills' when you take a sleeping pill. Benzodiazepines can also be prescribed as a muscle relaxant for injuries, as an anticonvulsant for epileptic fits and as a 'pre-med' before surgery. Everything in this book applies both to benzodiazepine tranquillisers and to benzodiazepine hypnotics. A full list of data (up to March 1991) appears at the back of the book.

The following list shows the benzodiazepines in the different categories (as at March 1991).

Chemical or generic name	Brand name
Long-acting anxiolytics	
Bromazepam	Lexotan
Chlordiazepoxide	Librium
	Limbitrol
	Tropium
Clobazam	Frisium
Clorazepate	Tranxene

Chemical or generic name	Brand name
Diazepam	Alupram
	Atensine
	Diazemuls (given as a 'pre-med')
	Solis
	Stesolid
	Tensium
	Valium
Medazepam	Nobrium
Medium-acting anxiolytics	
Alprazolam	Xanax
Short-acting anxiolytics	
Lorazepam	Almazine
	Ativan
Oxazepam	Oxanid
Long-acting hypnotics	
Flunitrazepam	Rohypnol
Flurazepam	Dalmane
Nitrazepam	Mogadon
	Nitrados
	Remnos
	Somnite
	Unisomnia
Medium-acting hypnotics	
Loprazolam	Dormonoct
Lormetazepam	
Temazepam	Normison
Short-acting hypnotics	
Triazolam	Halcion

(NB Clonazepam, brand name Rivotril, is an anti–epileptic drug, and midazolam, brand name Hypnovel, is used intravenously.)

There are other tranquillisers and hypnotics outside the benzo-diazepine group, such as Equanil (meprobamate), Welldorm (chloral betaine), Noctec (chloral hydrate), Buspar (buspirone hydrochlor) and Zimovane (zopiclone). The Martindale of 1982 said this of zopiclone: 'though differing structurally, it is reported to have hypnotic and sedative activity similar to that of the benzo-diazepines'.

HOW DO BENZODIAZEPINES WORK?

To understand how benzodiazepines work, we have to look at the workings of the brain. In the brain we have natural calming-down substances, called GABA, which stop the nerve cells from firing off, and reduce our adrenaline and our excitement. Benzodiaze-pines work by taking the place of GABA. The more we rely on benzodiazepines, the more we are suppressing our natural substances. We need these less and less, until they become obsolete.

Everyone has hang-ups and dislikes, or become nervous in certain situations. I call it our own vulnerability. It is part of our personality. But when we have been taking tranquillisers our vul-nerability can be magnified. So a person who doesn't like crowded places may become agoraphobic. Someone who suffers from giddy spells may find that the spells worsen, perhaps developing into vertigo. And those who are awkward about meeting strangers may find they can't even talk to the milkman or postman.

Why does this happen? The answer lies in the suppression of the natural calming-down processes. When we didn't take drugs we had our own built-in coping mechanism to fall back on to give us that extra boost, so that we could ride the situation and put on a 'stiff upper lip'. But the tranquillisers take over that coping mechanism and strip us of our own confidence, so we come to rely on the tranquillisers for that inner strength. When we have reached our tolerance level or when we stop taking the drug we have neither the tranquilliser to help us to cope nor our own resources—our nerves and emotions are 'raw'.

WHAT BENZODIAZEPINES DO NOT DO

Whether you are taking benzodiazepines as a tranquilliser for anxiety or as a sleeping pill for insomnia, they do *not* cure the problem for which they are prescribed.

The tranquilliser you swallow is *not* the answer to your anxiety and stress in the long run. How can it be? How can a pill help you cope with a crying baby? Or stop your marriage from breaking up? Or help with the presure of work? Or pay your bills? It can't, of course. After you've swallowed your pill the baby will still cry, your husband might still walk out, your work will still be on your desk, your bills will still be sent to you. Life will still go on, and the pressures will still be there. All you are doing is anaesthetising your emotions—not dealing with them. By swallowing the pill you are giving yourself a false sense of security. You may feel better for a day or two. You may find you don't shout as much, you may feel as if you are a nicer person to live with. Pop a pill and you feel as if you can cope with any of the pressures at work. Who are you kidding? Only yourself!

The hypnotic you take to help stop your insomnia will not give you a proper night's sleep. When we go to sleep naturally, we go through four stages. In the first stage we feel drowsy and then we drop off. In the second stage we are in a medium slumber and are unconscious of what is going on around us. In the third and fourth stages we are in a deep sleep, or slow wave sleep (SWS), when the activity of the brain is at its lowest. Thereafter, we enter rapid eye movement sleep (REM), during which we dream. Our brain activity and our eye movements are similar to when we are awake. We are creating fantasies—dreams. If we don't go into a deep slumber and experience REM, we don't feel as if we've had a good night's sleep, and we can be irritable or aggressive when we wake up.

When we take sleeping pills we do not enter the third and fourth stages of sleep and we often do not dream, so, although we've been asleep, it is not the same sleep as natural sleep.

WE ARE NOT TOLD THE WHOLE STORY

When we enter the doctor's surgery we may be at our most vulnerable. We are feeling ill, we are worried about our ailments, and we don't understand why we feel so poorly. On top of that we may have a host of problems at home or at work, which we more than likely feel is irrelevant to our physical illness. In other words, we are going through a bad time.

We may say to the doctor: 'I can't cope', or 'I'm always irritable', or 'I've got palpitations', or 'I can't concentrate'. These are all expressions of anxiety.

We may ask the doctor: 'Why am I feeling ill?' We want an explanation. He may not give us an answer—he may just say: 'Here's something that'll help you.' And he may write out a prescription for one or more of the benzodiazepines. He may not even tell us it is a tranquilliser. We may go away in a contented oblivion, believing that the pills are just something to help our rash, menstrual problem or nausea. We may have no idea the pills are for anxiety.

Possibly the doctor may not mention that benzodiazepines are dependency forming, and that if we take the pills for more than a couple of weeks we may suffer some withdrawal symptoms when we stop. Over the years, I have helped thousands of people with their addiction at TRANX. One of the questions I sometimes ask a new client is 'were you told by your doctor that benzodiazepines are addictive?' The answer most of the time is 'no'. Nor are we told a sleeping pill will have little or no effect after a few days. Nor that the effect of the tranquilliser wears off after a certain amount of time and that we may need more of the same drugs and/or stronger drugs to get the same effect. This means we have reached our tolerance level. We take the doctor's advice that the pills should make us feel better, and we are totally unaware of the consequences.

Today the medical profession should be fully aware of the risks of benzodiazepines. The Committee on Safety of Medicines report in 1988 told doctors that the drug can be addictive after a short period. It warned them that a hypnotic should not be given for longer than three days, and (as we saw on page 9) that a tranquilliser should not be prescribed for longer than four weeks. It recommended that the drug should not be used to treat depression or anxiety associated with depression, phobic or obsessional states, chronic psychosis or even in bereavements. It also warned that the drug can lead to suicide.

Yet even with these warnings and precautions, some doctors can't kick the habit of prescribing benzodiazepines. Over 23 million prescriptions were written in 1988,[18] making benzodiazepines still the best selling drug on the market, even beating antibiotics. It has been estimated that 3.5 million people in the United Kingdom are taking the drug for up to six months and 1.2 million people are on it for over a year.

WHY PEOPLE HAVE BEEN PRESCRIBED TRANQUILLISERS

At TRANX we dealt with an average of 2000 enquiries a month from benzodiazepine addicts. Some of the reasons why they were initially prescribed benzodiazepines were:

bereavement
emotional upsets
nursing sick wife
    after operation
husband's accident
socialising
after flu virus
dry eyes
hysterectomy
alcoholic problem
alcoholic father
sex abuse
stomach trouble
business problems
handicapped child
shiftwork
bankruptcy
demanding mother
scared of dying
lack of confidence
homelessness
mother committed
    suicide

jury service
work pressure
loss of hearing
interview nerves
dizziness
stroke
active/crying baby
shyness
childhood insecurity
isolation
family problems
floater in eye
broken neck
changed job
violent husband
prison
infertility
cystitis
cooker blew up
claustrophobia
illness
post–natal
    depression

exam nerves
fatal illness
disc trouble
divorce
menopause
bad fall
rugby injury
rape
car crash
headaches
back pain
mastectomy
thyroid
driving test
cat died
redundancy
hay fever
vertigo
palpitations
moving home
asthma
retirement
abortion

Most of these problems are hardly reasons to be put on tranquillisers—they are life events which need to be talked through, and not subdued with pills.

IT'S A VICIOUS CIRCLE

Once on the benzodiazepine 'merry-go-round' it may be hard to get off. You may go to the doctor because you can't sleep. The doctor may prescribe you sleeping pills, usually benzodiazepines. You take the sleeping pill that night and bliss—you're asleep. The following night you take the pill and again you sleep. You may sleep well for several nights, but eventually the time comes when you end up lying awake again—even after taking your 'magical' sleeping pill. So you return to the doctor, telling him that you are taking the pills but you still can't sleep. So the doctor gives you stronger or more pills.

A similar situation can arise when you take benzodiazepines for anxiety. You may go to the doctor because you have headaches, shout at the children or argue with your husband—life in general is miserable. The doctor may give you benzodiazepine tranquillisers to calm you down. You take the pills and may feel better for a while. You don't shout so much, you are able to cope better and those awful headaches have gone. But after a short time you may begin to crave your tranquilliser sooner. You return to the doctor, tell him your problem and he may give you a stronger pill or may tell you to take them more often.

What has happened in both these cases is that you have reached your tolerance level. And there is no limit. I was taking sleeping pills at hourly intervals throughout the night, plus drugs throughout the day—and I still could not sleep.

But why don't we say 'No more pills, thank you doctor.' Firstly, we may be dependent. In a short time we can become 'hooked'. We may need our tranquillisers and sleeping pills just as much as the drug addict needs his fix. Also, our reactions may have begun to slow down: we can't think clearly, and we may feel like a zombie. When we are told we need more or stronger pills, we might not *want* to take more because we know it isn't right, but we are unable to disagree—we just cannot assert ourselves anymore.

Betty was prescribed benzodiazepines for post-natal depression. Her drugs weren't stopped when her baby grew up, but instead her prescription was increased over the years and she found herself more and more enmeshed in the tranquilliser trap. 'I just didn't have the incentive to do anything in life', she says. 'I hated the fact that I took these tablets, I just hated it, but nobody could help me, I couldn't get off them. I couldn't give them up. I couldn't stop taking them. I couldn't cope with it. I had to take these tablets and I hated them so much.'

Liz, a bright intelligent young mother, was pregnant with her second child. At that time her marriage was breaking up. She went to the doctor and told her of her problem. The doctor's answer was to prescribe benzodiazepines. On leaving the surgery the doctor asked Liz to return in a few weeks' time. Liz did go back and this time she told the doctor her husband had moved out for a week. The doctor asked 'Was it any easier?' Liz replied, 'It was'. 'It would be', said the doctor, 'you haven't got so much to do.' Liz was dumbfounded at this reply. She was hurt that the doctor saw her as a woman who couldn't cope with being a mother. But she didn't stand up for herself—instead she said nothing, 'because you don't when you are on the pills', says Liz 'you don't say anything.'

We have been conditioned by our parents and by society to believe that whatever the doctor says must be right. We don't think to question him. In the eyes of so many people he is 'God'.

June, a wealthy middle-class woman, took tranquillisers and sleeping pills for thirty years. At one point she was on nineteen pills a day, though not all of them were benzodiazepines. She explains: 'I didn't question it, I didn't think to question it. I assumed I needed these pills. The doctor said I will be on them for the rest of my life. If your doctor tells you that, you believe him. When you are young, you are told the doctor is "God"—you've got to be respectful and do as you are told.'

Suzanne also had complete faith in her doctor in New Zealand. She emigrated from England when she married a New Zealander, and shortly after arriving there she became pregnant. But the new baby, new life and new marriage were too much for her to cope with all at once. She suffered post-natal depression, and the doctor readily prescribed benzodiazepines. Suzanne took the drug because 'the doctor was always right, he was sort of a "God". You didn't argue, the doctor said this was the best thing for you. It was practically a case of "yes sir".'

The 'merry-go-round' of pill-taking might not stop with benzo-diazepines. The first benzodiazepine you take might be the start of an endless cocktail of drugs. After a time benzodiazepines may cause depression, so very often an antidepressant will be prescribed. But the drug can also cause other side-effects, and so you may be given other drugs because your doctor, like June's, may wrongly diagnose the side-effect as another illness.

LABELLED

Once you've been prescribed benzodiazepines you may be labelled as someone who needs drugs to sleep, or as unable to cope with life. You are more at risk of being given other mood-altering drugs on another occasion than someone who hasn't had tranquillisers or sleeping pills. When the GP gives you a prescription for benzodiazepines he may also write down in your medical history that you are 'suffering with nerves', 'neurotic' or have a 'personality disorder'. That label will always hang over you. Even if you change to a new doctor, when he reads your notes he will have an impression of you before you've even entered his surgery. He will expect to see an anxious person walk through his door. We all love to pigeon-hole people, and doctors are no exception. But the fact is your personality cannot be properly assessed whilst you are on the drugs, because the drugs may change your personality. This will be further discussed in Part Two.

HOW WE FALL INTO THE TRANQUILLISER TRAP

My story: on benzodiazepines for seventeen years

If anyone should have gone on pills, perhaps it should have been my then husband but I was the one who went to the doctor that day. My husband was good-looking and intelligent, but he had a

violent temper. He worked sporadically so we were never financially secure, and often I didn't have enough money to buy my four
young children food. It was because of an argument about money
that I ended up on tranquillisers.

I had an appointment for the dentist. Although I went on the
National Health, a charge had just been introduced. I asked my husband if he could pay the bill, but my request only aroused his violent
nature. He hit me. It wasn't the first time, but this time his blows
brought me to the doctor's surgery. The doctor cleaned my wounds
while I cried. But the tears weren't only for the cuts and bruises—
they were for my broken marriage. I was scared and desperate.
When the last wound had been treated, my doctor wrote out a prescription for benzodiazepines.

Frank's story: on tranquillisers for nine years

Frank was a family man. He loved his wife and his two young children. They lived in a semi-detached house in the suburbs of London.
Frank was proud of his job as salesman for one of the top fashion
companies in England. The company saw Frank as their blue-eyed
boy and began to rely on his expertise. He was called upon to deal
with their most eminent customers.

Everything was fine until the company was taken over. Then the
company changed both its policies and its standards. Frank began to
work longer hours. He started to miss meal breaks—instead he just
grabbed a quick coffee and a sandwich, and because he got home at
10 or 11 p.m., he felt it was too late to have a cooked meal. Sunday
became the only day he could try to relax. But, of course, he couldn't
unwind. Soon he began to lose his appetite. Eventually, he went to
his GP who prescribed him tranquillisers.

Margaret's story: on tranquillisers for fifteen years

Margaret was a bright and intelligent woman. She worked as a
researcher for a television company where she often did shift work.
She was successfully married to a businessman. Financially they
were very comfortable. On the face of it they looked as if they had
everything, but they had one thing missing in their relationship:

children. Margaret found it difficult to conceive, so, desperate for a child, she and her husband started plans to adopt. Then, to their delight, she became pregnant.

When the baby girl was born, Margaret and he husband were overjoyed. Margaret decided to give up her job with the television company because she wanted to bring up her own child and not employ a childminder. During that time her husband was often away on business, so Margaret found herself alone in a large house with a newborn baby. Because she had worked shifts she hadn't met many of her neighbours, and she became lonely. She felt she could physically keep busy, but she didn't know how to occupy her mind. Because she felt she had everything a woman could want—a beautiful and healthy daughter, a loving husband and a nice house, she felt guilty that she was feeling low and depressed. As her guilt increased, she sank further into depression. Then, when her daughter was six months old, she went to the doctor who told her she had post-natal depression. He prescribed her antidepressants which later led to a variety of tranquillisers.

CAN TAKING TRANQUILLISERS RUN IN THE FAMILY?

We learn from our parents. When a child grows up in a family where one or both of the parents take pills regularly, the child may believe that taking drugs is a normal and natural thing to do. If the child always sees a bottle of tranquillisers or sleeping pills in the medicine cabinet, when the child becomes an adult and hits a crisis he or she may think of tranquillisers or sleeping pills as the way out of the situation.

This happened to Daniel. His father had been on tranquillisers and so had his grandfather. Daniel had seen through his father and grandfather that when life became tough, tranquillisers were there to help you through. Other families had alcohol in the house—his family had tranquillisers. When Daniel was sixteen years old and studying for his 'O' levels his parents and teachers expected him to do well, but he found the pressure of studying too great. He suffered exam nerves. So to help himself get over his worries he went to his doctor

for tranquillisers, and was given them. And so Daniel became the
third generation in his family to take tranquillisers for life events.

Paul had also seen his parents take tranquillisers, but they took
pills to give them the courage to commit crimes. Paul was sixteen
years old when his father asked him to accompany him on a bank
robbery. 'The first time I ever took a tranquilliser was when my
mother gave it to me. She said to me I was anxious about things (the
bank robbery) and she said "take this, it'll make you feel better". I
suppose all my life I've seen her take tranquillisers. She was on them
since they first came out. She was on all sorts of drugs from when she
was fifteen years old. I thought I was doing the right thing, taking
tranquillisers, because my mother had always done it.'

Even when the child had seen how much sadness tranquillisers can
bring to a family, she or he may still take them regardless. This happened to David's niece, Sharon. Sharon had watched her uncle
become more and more ill on tranquillisers, until he eventually committed suicide. She had also observed her mother's struggle to wean
herself off benzodiazepines. And yet when she hit a crisis in her own
life, she turned to the pill bottle for help. Sometimes it seems children don't learn by their parents' mistakes, but instead carry on the
trait.

However, not every child is like Sharon, some who have seen
their parents suffer from the effects of these pills will reject them. My
daughter Maira was offered benzodiazepines when her newborn
baby was taken into hospital with breathing problems, but she
refused, saying 'I have learnt from my mother's experience what
these pills can do to you.'

II

WHY DOCTORS PRESCRIBE
TRANQUILLISERS

'My doctor gives me pills to put him out of my misery.'
Australian tranquilliser addict

It may seem shocking, but for nearly thirty years most doctors have been in the dark about the effects of benzodiazepines. Although some doctors murmured concern from its birth, the medical profession as a whole didn't really recognise that the drug caused side-effects, dependence or withdrawal problems until the Committee on Safety of Medicines report in January 1988. In fact, most doctors believed when they were writing out a prescription for benzodiazepines that they were giving the best treatment. After all, benzodiazepines had been hailed as being safe, in that the patient couldn't overdose as with barbiturates, and for many years there was no firm medical evidence that the drug was addictive except in large doses. Nor did the doctors understand about a patient reaching his or her tolerance level—they simply thought, when the drug no longer seemed to work, that the patient's original ailment was coming back. Unfortunately some doctors still believe this today.

Because a drug in the benzodiazepine group was seen as a 'pill that could cure all ills', from backache to the break-up of a marriage, doctors became addicted to prescribing it—and some still are, even in the light of recent medical evidence. Eighty per cent of benzodiazepine users claim they had been started on the drug by their general practitioner.[19] What's more, a survey carried out in 1988 by Dr Hunt, Director of Health Studies at Sussex University, of GPs in

Brighton found that one in seven scripts contained a prescription for a tranquilliser in the benzodiazepine group. And 7.5 per cent of those scripts contained more than one prescription for benzodiazepines.[20]

One doctor explains why some physicians are reluctant to give up writing out prescriptions for tranquillisers and hypnotics. 'You have to give up one of your best weapons . . . the doctor's training encourages him to be rather dependent on his prescription pad, which does not help him to make proper use of himself as a person. Medicinal drugs are so powerful and at times so effective that it is natural for the doctor to put his faith in them, rather than in himself—which is where the patient really wants it.'

Most of us have been brought up with the idea the doctor not only heals wounds but also can patch up our emotional problems. Yet he may have had very little training on how to counsel. When we enter his surgery in a flood of tears, blurting out expressions like 'I can't cope', 'I feel depressed' and 'life is too much for me', the doctor may find it difficult to know how to handle the situation. In other words, *he* can't cope. Dr Bhatt explains: 'If a patient comes to me with an emotional problem that I couldn't cope with as a doctor, I'll think I'll give her a tranquilliser. At least she will not be so tense and anxious, she will be able to face up to her problems—it is the philosophy of desperation for the doctor.' In effect, what the doctor is doing is treating himself.

But by taking the tranquilliser the patient will be subduing the symptoms of her emotions, and not facing up to them at all. In my view, the doctor is giving the wrong treatment. When doctors are confronted by highly emotional men or women I believe it would be better to refer them to a counsellor or to find an alternative therapy, and to leave the prescription pad well alone. Some counselling, psychotherapy and group therapy has at last been integrated into our healthcare system. But ten years ago it was virtually unheard of to go to therapy, as Dr Bhatt explains. 'Then there was only the doctor, the patient and the prescription pad.' Even with the alternative therapies available today, some doctors find it difficult to accept them, as they can seem like a threat to their own professionalism.

Dr Bhatt also believes that physicians write out prescriptions not only for therapeutic reasons but also for symbolic reasons. The GP wants to be seen as a caring doctor, as someone who will help the patient. 'I must prove to this person that I care for him/her, therefore I will give him/her a prescription.' When a doctor gives out a prescription he is saying to the patient: 'I like you sufficiently to say you can have these drugs'. The doctor wants to be seen as the person who reaches out to the patient, but the only way he may be able to reach out is by giving drugs. If he passes his patient on to another form of treatment, like counselling, he may feel he is not fulfilling his helping role.

Also, the doctor sometimes may feel pressurised by the patient to dish out the pills. Time and time again doctors say to me: 'It's all very well saying don't give your patients tranquillisers, but what do you do with the patients who insist on getting their pills?' One GP told me of a patient who would not listen to him when he suggested she came off her pills. 'What does it matter to you', she said to him, 'they aren't doing me any harm. What's all the fuss about?' And another patient insisted he had a heart complaint when the doctor knew his symptoms were because of the tranquillisers he was taking.

I know many patients do plead with their doctors for their quota of pills, and some patients may go as far as to leave a practice and join another one to get them. I did. I left one doctor who wouldn't give me all my pills for another who was more lenient when it came to prescribing pills. Some tranquilliser addicts will get extra pills from doctors who they are not officially registered with, by pretending to be out of their area. The reason why we are so insistent about getting our tranquillisers or sleeping pills isn't because we want to abuse the taking of these drugs, as some physicians believe; quite simply it's because we are hooked, through no fault of our own. We have reached our tolerance level.

Maybe prescribing tranquillisers has been in the doctor's mind before the patient has even entered his surgery. Advertisements enticing doctors to prescribe certain drugs are scattered among the features in his medical journals. Headlines such as these try to catch the GP's attention: '. . . helps calm anxious patients', '. . . when the plea is "I can't cope".' Diana Wyndham, Research Officer with the University of New South Wales, Australia, wrote in the magazine *New Doctor* that 'It cannot be denied that advertising considerably influences general practitioners. In fact, for most, commercially biased promotional literature is almost their only source of drug

information. The fact that Australian doctors prescribe some benzodiazepines almost entirely by trade name supports this claim.'

An interesting story is told of one GP who was visited by a representative from a drugs company who recommended a certain drug.
This drug, however, had just been proved to be of no value and possibly dangerous. He showed the representative the door and
promised himself never to allow another visit of this kind—and he
kept his promise. Furthermore, he avoided reading all advertisements in the medical journals. The result of 22 years in practice
without the influence of advertisements but with careful reading of
the *Lancet, British Medical Journal* and the *Drug and Therapeutics Bulletin* is that this doctor has been able to avoid the new, possibly bad,
dangerous or more expensive drugs prescribed by his colleagues.[21]

The prescribing habits of doctors are also affected by how long the
surgery is open. 'The longer the surgery hours,' says Diana
Wyndham, 'the greater the prescription rate.' The doctor is under
great pressure over the amount of time he allocates to each patient.
He may prescribe drugs to cut short appointments. The average time
spent with a doctor is 8 minutes 14 seconds—hardly enough time to
discuss your life-long problems.

If we look back over the facts, maybe it's not so much the patients
who have abused benzodiazepines, but the doctors who have abused
the prescribing of them, thereby producing an iatrogenic disease—a
disease created by the medical profession. I am not putting the blame
for the tranquilliser addiction problem at the doctor's surgery door.
How can you blame someone who didn't know and didn't understand? But what does worry me is those doctors who are still
turning a blind eye to the evidence that surrounds them, and who are
still carrying on the often needless prescribing of benzodiazepines
today.

PART TWO

SYMPTOMS

I

WHO AM I?

*'I am thirty-nine years old. Since the age of fourteen I have been on
tranquillisers. I have married, had a daughter and divorced, how do I
know who I am?'*
Carol

This confused state is very common among tranquilliser addicts. We
don't know who we are because we are not in control of our
emotions. We are given tranquillisers to help us avoid the anguish
and pain we are experiencing, and with time our emotions are buried
so deep that we can't feel at all. Then it isn't just the painful and
fearful emotions which are blocked, but the happy ones as well.

Our natural emotions are so important in understanding ourselves. We need our emotions—sorrow, love, hate, worry,
happiness—to tell us how to react to a situation and the people
around us, and how we respond gives us clues to our personality.
Just everyday events tell us something about ourselves: some people
get uptight when driving a car; others dislike being in crowded
shops; some people shout at their children over the tiniest incident;
others cry at the end of a tear-jerking film. Our character is formed
like a jigsaw. Piece by piece, all the situations we encounter show us
different sides which gradually slot together until eventually we
have a complete picture of ourselves. But for someone who takes
tranquillisers, some of the pieces of their jigsaw are missing. The
drug has wiped them out or covered them up.

The spiral of addiction can start when we are given pills to stop the
worry or fear that is gnawing away inside us. Soon we find we may
need more pills for less traumatic situations until we may be taking

pills just to do everyday things. We may end up swallowing pills simply to function—to start the day, to go shopping, to go to a business meeting, to cope with an unexpected problem, to go out to dinner with friends and to go to sleep.

Eventually, we may stop functioning. We may give up going to the supermarket, at work we may hand in our notice or we may be given the sack, we may reject the responsibility of looking after our children, we may not go out, we may not open the front door to callers, we may not invite friends into our homes, we might have lost most of our friends anyway, we may not cook and we may not make love. We lose interest in everything, and instead we escape into our bottle of pills, only to become imprisoned by them.

Vivian and Liz

Vivian, 38 years old, is an intelligent and attractive woman. She has a high-powered job with an embassy, where a large proportion of her day is spent translating and being an interpreter. Her work also involved travelling—to her hopping on a plane used to be as simple as taking the bus.

She also enjoyed a busy social life. 'I was going out all the time. I was going to theatres and I was travelling. I had a boyfriend who used to fly a little two-seater aeroplane. I would fly with him even though he didn't have his pilot's licence—he was still learning, but I thought, great, I am going to do some flying.'

Vivian had many boyfriends. Eventually she had a love affair with Tony. After a while they decided to live together but the relationship was always volatile. Soon Vivian became pregnant and gave birth to a girl.

The relationship between Vivian and Tony didn't improve with the arrival of the baby, so when the baby was three months old Vivian decided that the best thing to do was to leave Tony. She found a flat for herself and the baby, and continued to work. Although she was stretched bringing up her daughter and working, she found she could cope. Her work was stimulating and she adored her baby, devoting every spare moment she had to her. For three years Vivian was happy.

Then her sister committed suicide by taking an overdose of

prescribed pills. Vivian was devastated. 'I couldn't cope with the pain', she says. After that it was as if her own life fell apart. She couldn't cope with her demanding job, she couldn't cope with being a one-parent family. All her pressures now seemed too great to endure. So she went along to her doctor who prescribed tranquillisers.

Vivian took tranquillisers for just over three years, and in that time she slowly changed. 'And the worst part was', says Vivian, 'I didn't even notice I was changing. It was a very, very slow process. In the end, I could no longer face going into shops, I was always giving my daughter some kind of excuse, just so I would not have to go out. I couldn't even take her to the park where she could play. Having to tell fibs to my daughter hurt most. I isolated myself more and more and accepted no more invitations. I just wanted to stay at home, dreading the day the fear would penetrate even that last sanctuary left to me.

'Every day I fought with myself in order to go to work, going and returning, praying to God just to give me the strength to reach the bus stop or the underground station, just to give my exhausted limbs strength to walk me home, just enough stamina to have a bath or brush my teeth. Going out would paralyse me with fear; groping for my tablets I would hope their effect would set in before something horrible and irreversible would happen. I didn't want any sexual relationships—I didn't *feel*. And above all I didn't think I was worthy of any relationship. I felt old, I felt so horrible about myself. I no longer had any confidence as a human being, I didn't have any confidence as a woman, I didn't have any confidence as a mother.

'I became totally obsessed with the drugs. I could only think of me and my drugs, my life and my worth. I even lost the feeling I had for my daughter. I couldn't feel love any more, and this caused the biggest guilt feeling. I would look at her and say I love you and then I'd say: what is love? I didn't have any feelings. Morbid thoughts of something terrible happening to me or my child and close family would never be far away. I thought, if this is life then just put the clock on fast and let it go by because I didn't want to face it any more.

'At work I found I couldn't concentrate. I used to have to do a lot of simultaneous translation, and I would look at the person who was talking and I couldn't absorb it. It was like floating. I also have to meet a lot of people through my work. I didn't like it because I would wonder what would happen if I can't do what they want, or maybe I can't think properly. It wasn't only my brain that seemed as if it was going, but I slowed down too. My cousin said to me, "You are talking in slow motion, you are moving in slow motion. Is the film going at the right speed?"'

This is a typical example of how the drugs took everything away from Vivian. She changed from a confident, fun, adventurous woman into someone who was timid and scared of life. She lost her confidence at work because she couldn't concentrate. She lost her confidence as a mother, while in the past she had coped well. Love and feelings evaporated from her until she had neither the natural mother's love nor feelings for other people, which in turn made her feel guilty, encouraging feelings of depression. She no longer had the confidence to have relationships with men because of her low self-esteem. So she became more and more obsessed with her drugs and fell deeper and deeper into depression. In the end her drugs took over her life.

Liz explains how tranquillisers affected her life. 'The doctor changed my sleeping tablets. I stayed on them for ten years. In the beginning, the first couple of weeks, I felt really good, obviously I was on a "high". I slept well. But then it wasn't long, within two or three months, I found I couldn't get out of the front door in the mornings to go to work. I kept saying to myself, "I must go, I'll be late." Anxiety was building up on anxiety. Soon I jacked in my job as a school secretary which I had had for five years. I told my boss I couldn't do the job any more because I didn't know what I was doing. For ten years I experienced one big long anxiety trip, every minute of the day. It got to the stage where I didn't even know how to get up out of bed, I would hit the walls. When I told my doctor, he prescribed antidepressants, which acted as an "upper" on me. So then the first thing I did when I got up was to take my "uppers". I would look at the clock and think in half an hour I will be feeling a little more human. Then I would go through the motions—getting the children out of bed, running their baths and making their packed lunches. But gradually over the years that all stopped. I got as far as getting the bread out and all the fillings but I couldn't actually make the sandwiches. Soon I stopped running their baths, and I got the children to make their own beds because I couldn't quite manage that any more, it seemed to take so long. Then I stopped cooking, I stopped sewing, I just stopped doing everything.'

Liz is a typical example of how the spiral of addiction can get out of control because of the lack of understanding about the withdrawal symptoms of benzodiazepines. Liz was prescribed sleeping tablets which not only created more anxiety but also depression in her. The doctor's remedy was to put her on antidepressants which heightened her depression, making her feel more and more of a failure. Now her doctor saw her as a depressive even though she was taking antidepressants.

Accepting we are addicted can be devastating. When June was told by her doctor that she was an addict, she replied: 'Don't be ridiculous, I don't inject anything into my arm. I take prescribed pills.' We might be taking legal drugs, we might even be taking the correct therapeutic dose, but we are still dependent.

Dr David Marjot, Consultant Psychiatrist at St Bernard's Hospital, London, explains addiction as 'the propensity to seek out and consume your drug of choice as the priority in your life'. And Dr Hallstrom, Consultant Psychiatrist, Charing Cross Hospital, believes: 'Basically someone who can't contemplate a day without tranquillisers must in some way be dependent'.[22] It is true that tranquilliser addicts often put their pills above everything else, but I believe there are two types of addicts. There is the Addict with the capital A, and the addict with the small a. The Addict with a capital A may take anything in order to help her through life—be it alcohol, heroin, tranquillisers, crack or glue. She may abuse the taking of the drug and she may top up with whatever comes to hand—prescribed pills, illegal drugs, alcohol, even cough syrup.

The addict with a small a may take more and more pills and *look* as if she is abusing the drug, but the reason she increases her dose is simply because she has reached her tolerance level. She has found herself trapped in a net, and doesn't know how to get out. Although she will not go out to seek other kinds of drugs to help her, she may sometimes turn to alcohol to 'top up', especially if she is unable to obtain a larger supply of pills from her doctor who may not understand what is happening.

Tranquilliser addicts are usually addicts with a small a. Here are some typical examples of addictive behaviour.

My addiction

When I was addicted to tranquillisers, I was working as a casualty receptionist in a London hospital. Every day I made sure that I had my pills on hand and a glass of water on my desk, so that if a situation came up which I found difficult to handle, my pills were there to help me cope.

Angela, a single woman

'For twenty years I never failed to go out without my phial of tranquillisers on me. I checked that phial before I checked my keys and my purse. I would have rather lost my cheque book and bank cards, so long as I had my pills. A thief could rob me of anything so long as he left me my pills.'

Martin, a married man with two children

'If I was going abroad on business for two days I would need six tranquillisers, but in case I had to stay longer I knew that six wouldn't be enough. So I would go to another doctor and get thirty tablets from him. I would always take more away with me than I needed. I never operated on being down to just two tablets and then going to the doctor the next day, in case there was a hitch. Even if I wasn't travelling abroad, I made sure I always had my pills with me. I always had some in the car. When I got my quota from the doctor I would divide them up—half in the bottle in the drawer in my bedside table and half in a phial in the glove compartment in the car. I was also deceitful about how many pills I took. I used to pretend to my wife I was only taking one pill when I was taking more.'

Martin is not alone when he admits to lying to his wife. We are so ashamed of taking tranquillisers that we want to hide our addiction. Some of us pretend to our spouse, relatives or friends that we are taking the therapeutic dose when we are taking many more pills, and others do not even admit to taking the drug at all.

We are secretive about our addiction because tranquillisers sap our confidence and self-esteem, so we are left feeling more insecure than someone who is not on drugs. We feel that by admitting we are dependent on pills we are accepting what we inwardly fear: that we are a failure. We are confessing, to those around us, we cannot go through life's ups and downs without the help of a drug, without the support of a 'crutch'. This feeling increases with each additional drug we are prescribed, as Liz explained in her account.

IS THERE AN ADDICTIVE PERSONALITY?

Can we put addiction down to personality or a certain type of person? Are addicts mainly weak-minded or subordinate?

Dr Peter Tyrer, Consultant Psychiatrist at St Charles Hospital, suggests there are two types of personality disorders associated with benzodiazepine dependence. The first group are those of 'an unstable mood and impulsive behaviour'. And the second group are 'the timid worriers or the anxious personality'.[23] If it were as clear-cut as that, wouldn't it make life easy for the doctor? All he would have to do is to sum up our character and if we weren't timid, unstable, impulsive or anxious he could happily write out a prescription for a benzodiazepine, knowing we wouldn't become addicted. But if only that were true. It's not.

Dr David Marjot warns: 'I have noticed there is a tendency to say that if you are of a particular psychological make-up you may be vulnerable to benzodiazepines; that is true to a point but it is only part of the explanation. There are some people who have curiously neurotic personality structures who come off benzodiazepines without any trouble, and there are people who seem very stable and were put on the drug for bereavement or loss of job who have an awful time coming off. I think we have to be very cautious about generalisation. The trouble is we often rush for explanations before we have any fundamental understanding of what's going on. The explanations are very superficial or often false.'

But there is a process of self-selection that influences who carries on taking the benzodiazepines once prescribed. Only 20 per cent of the people who are given a prescription for a month take them all—the rest put them down the drain, states Dr Heather Ashton. She believes that 'if you are a calm person the benzodiazepines will not have a nice effect on you, they may put you in a trance and you would feel as if you were only half there. Whereas if you are under a great deal of stress, agitated, anxious or worried, they do take a load off you, and bring you down to a more normal state—until you get tolerant to them.' In short, it's the old philosophy of one man's meat is another man's poison. Becoming dependent and experiencing withdrawal symptoms is down to the way we are made. Some people may take tranquillisers and then stop without any adverse effect. They are the lucky ones: others go through 'hell'. The question of who may become dependent and suffer withdrawal symptoms is still largely unanswered. It's the same as another problem which still baffles people: how some people can give up smoking without any trouble, whereas others can't kick the habit. For the same reason, it is also very risky to believe some people will *not* become dependent on tranquillisers, because we do not know who these people are until they stop taking the drug. For those who do end up suffering withdrawal symptoms, it's too late to say we made a mistake.

Although we cannot say, as yet, who will become addicted, I believe that the people who do become dependent on tranquillisers show three different types of dependency. There is the psychologically dependent person, the physically dependent person and lastly the person who is both physically and psychologically dependent.

Psychologically dependent

This person has a psychological craving for the drug. She needs the drug to make life easier, to stop her feeling the pain. Her *mind* needs the drug. This person may keep a bottle of tranquillisers in the bathroom cabinet just in case she can't sleep or life hits a crisis. Because the tranquillisers or sleeping pills are in easy reach, she feels she has her 'safety net'. Even after a psychologically dependent person has come off benzodiazepines she may not throw away the pills for some time.

Physically dependent

Her body craves for the drug. She needs the drug to function because her *body's* metabolism is dependent on it, but she is not psychologically attached to the drug. When the effects of the drug wears off, she may experience ill effects which are withdrawal symptoms. The only way she can alleviate these symptoms is to take the drug again. She may not want the drug but she feels so physically ill she has to take it in order to function.

Physically and psychologically dependent

Both her *body* and *mind* crave the drug. She may have an over-dependent character and may always be dependent on something or someone. She may not just be dependent on drugs, she may also be dependent on her husband, mother, children, an organisation like TRANX, or even a person with a strong personality. Her relationship with her family may be one of 'not being able to let go' and not letting them be independent. This dependent trait may go back to her childhood.

HOW CAN I TELL IF I'M ADDICTED?

First of all, don't be misguided into thinking that by taking a small amount of benzodiazepines you should not become dependent on the drug. Dr Marjot states: 'Benzodiazepines can produce dependence and this can occur on any doses within the therapeutic range.' And remember: dependence can occur after even a short period (from a few days to a couple of weeks) of taking any of the benzodiazepines.

Three psychologists from the Maudsley Hospital in London sum up dependence as characterised by four phenomena: tolerance, craving, dosage escalation and an abstinence syndrome in withdrawal.[24]

If any of the following statements apply to you, you may be dependent on your pills.

1. You have been taking tranquillisers or sleeping pills for a prolonged period.

2. You have asked your doctor to increase your dose.

3. You are taking doses larger than recommended.

4. You are getting extra pills from different doctors.

5. You always make sure you have an adequate supply of pills.

6. You always carry your pills with you 'just in case'.

7. You have taken one or two extra pills when you know you have to face a stressful situation.

8. The drug is interfering with your life—causing difficulties in family relationships, social life and work.

9. You have tried unsuccessfully to cut down your dose or to stop taking your pills altogether.

Next we look at side-effects and withdrawal.

II

SIDE-EFFECTS AND WITHDRAWAL SYMPTOMS

'If I had a white stick, people would know I was blind; if I had a deaf aid, people would know I was deaf; if I was in a wheelchair, people would know I was disabled; but there is no badge to indicate that I am staggering along the street under the influence of medically prescribed minor tranquillisers.'
David

'If drugs weren't powerful poisons, they wouldn't work', says Dr David Marjot. Benzodiazepines do cause side-effects and withdrawal symptoms. He goes on to say, 'you can't have your cake and eat it. You can't have the benefits of the drug without its dangers.' Whatever drug we take, there is the likelihood that it may have an adverse reaction with certain people—even the everyday aspirin may cause stomach ulcers in a few users. But when the doctor prescribes the drug he is gambling on his patient being at low risk.

IS THERE A DIFFERENCE BETWEEN SIDE-EFFECTS AND WITHDRAWAL SYMPTOMS?

The adverse reactions we may experience from benzodiazepines can be called either side-effects or withdrawal symptoms. Generally, if we are taking the drug the symptoms are called side-effects; and if we are coming off they are called withdrawal symptoms, when they are usually accentuated. However, we can become tolerant to the drug while we are taking it, and in that case, we are withdrawing while still on the drug. This can sometimes happen when a drug-user has taken the same dose for some time.

People who increase their dose one day and then go back on a lower dose the following day can be throwing themselves in and out of withdrawal. This can happen in a number of different circumstances. For instance, a woman who takes extra pills when she has to fly to her holiday destination, and then decides when she is lying on the beach in the sun that she does not need such a high dose, may end up feeling ill because of withdrawal. Or perhaps the general practitioner tells his patient to take extra pills on a 'bad' day. When the patient goes back to her normal dose she may find she isn't feeling well, which again may be withdrawal. 'Upping' and 'downing' the dose only confuses the body and mind.

Unfortunately in many cases, though not all, the adverse reactions may become more severe or magnified for some time after we have come off the drugs completely. This is basically because we no longer have the drug to dampen down the symptoms. The way withdrawal symptoms affect us in recovery is discussed in Part Three.

Some doctors like to put the physical and psychological side-effects and/or withdrawal symptoms into different categories, but I see them as very much interrelated. For instance, you may feel physically ill with stomach problems or migraine, but this illness is due to your psychological fear or anxiety; or you may be shaking because you are worried.

THE SYMPTOMS

There are a great variety of possible symptoms; those described here are the most common. However no-one experiences them all. They can come and go, and then return again, until eventually they should disappear during the recovery process. First we look at the psychological symptoms.

Lack of motivation

Maybe the first side-effect that we notice when we are taking tranquillisers and/or sleeping pills is that we have no motivation to do anything. Ordinary everyday events which most people don't even think about are very difficult for us. We have to ask ourselves 'How am I going to get up?' 'How am I going to prepare the breakfast?'

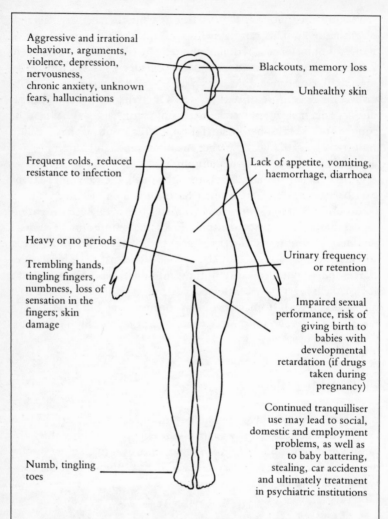

Aggressive and irrational behaviour, arguments, violence, depression, nervousness, chronic anxiety, unknown fears, hallucinations

Blackouts, memory loss

Unhealthy skin

Frequent colds, reduced resistance to infection

Lack of appetite, vomiting, haemorrhage, diarrhoea

Heavy or no periods

Urinary frequency or retention

Trembling hands, tingling fingers, numbness, loss of sensation in the fingers; skin damage

Impaired sexual performance, risk of giving birth to babies with developmental retardation (if drugs taken during pregnancy)

Continued tranquilliser use may lead to social, domestic and employment problems, as well as to baby battering, stealing, car accidents and ultimately treatment in psychiatric institutions

Numb, tingling toes

WHERE DO TRANQUILLISERS TAKE THEIR TOLL?

(Apart from specifically female problems, these effects can be experienced by both men and women)

'How am I going to get to work or the children to school?' We are not functioning properly, and this lethargic condition makes us feel like a zombie. We soon realise the only way we can get up in the morning to prepare breakfast and get ourselves ready for the day is to take a pill. Swallowing the pill is like turning the key on a wind-up doll—it enables us to get going.

There may be no place in our life for our child to have a party or go to the park, for friends to visit, for holidays or outings, and socialising may become a strain. In fact, many of the activities we used to enjoy we don't even attempt any more. Betty was prescribed tranquillisers for post-natal depression. For eighteen years she brought up her two sons in a tranquilliser haze.

'I was like a zombie. I didn't want to do anything and as the years went by it got worse. It was very difficult bringing up a couple of boys when you are drugged. Everything was such an effort because I was always tired. For nearly eighteen years virtually all I did was to get up, see the boys off to school, come home and lie on the sofa. I'd spend the entire day lying down. I only got up when I had to—when my husband came in at lunch-time from work, then I would make him a very quick snack. I'd never cook, it was always quick meals'.

'The kids were kept clean and fed but they were never taken out a great deal. They hardly ever had their friends over and we never had parties—I just couldn't cope with things like that. I didn't have any friends either. I didn't speak to anybody, so we'd never socialise, and really I am a very friendly person, but then I didn't feel well enough to do those things. Although I got up and dressed, I had no interest in clothes. My husband would say to me, "Come on, let's go out." "I've got nothing to wear," I'd reply. "I'll buy you something," he would say, but I'd reply, "What's the point? I don't go anywhere." I just put the same clothes on. I'd wash them, but they were the same clothes. I didn't have any incentive to go shopping.'

'I hardly ever cleaned my house, I just let it go. Like with everything—I just let everything go. I couldn't cope. I'd get confused. Then, of course, it's a vicious circle: because I felt so dreadful, I had to take another pill to operate, which only made me more depressed. It's a wonder I didn't commit suicide. Funny I never even thought about that. I didn't even have the thinking mind to do that. Just like a zombie.'

Betty gave up on life and spent days lying down. Everything was too much trouble for her—meals, her husband's lunch, the children's outings and so on. It was as if she had slowed down and turned herself off. Lack of motivation ties in with being depressed. She was given the drug for post-natal depression, but over the years, as with Liz, she totally lost her self-confidence and self-esteem and felt a failure, making her depression worse and worse. But her doctor at the time was saying she was suffering from an endogenous (basic) depression set off by her post-natal depression, and therefore she needed the drugs to help her through.

Increased anxiety

Benzodiazepines are supposed to be an anti-anxiety drug but, ironically, they can increase anxiety, both when we are taking the drug and more so during the coming-off period when we are learning to deal with life by ourselves, without a 'crutch'. When the drug gives the opposite of the desired effect, doctors often refer to it as a rebound reaction. However, I view it as a consequence of tolerance to the drug.

I have found that this paradoxical effect happens because when we take the drug we are stripped of our own natural coping mechanism, so instead of becoming less anxious, we become more anxious. Dr Heather Ashton agrees, as she has found from her research that benzodiazepines do make it more difficult for us to learn alternative strategies for coping with stress. Also the drugs soon lose their ability to reduce anxiety, and may even make it worse because of tolerance and withdrawal effects.[25]

Doris had never considered herself to be a very anxious person. In fact, when she came to talk to me she prided herself on how she used to cope with running the family, going out to work to do a responsible voluntary job, having dinner parties and meeting her husband's business acquaintances. But Doris and her husband decided to divorce. To ease the trauma of the break-up of the marriage, her doctor prescribed benzodiazepines.

Doris was still taking the drugs five years later when she remarried. But now she could not cope with anything in life. 'Suddenly I was aware', she says, 'that over the years I hadn't wanted to go out and I didn't go out.' Her confidence had eroded—she was frightened of answering the telephone and of callers at her front door. She found she couldn't cope with meeting her new husband's business colleagues or her son's friends. She even got to the stage where she would be in tears over writing out the weekly shopping list. 'The drug just destroyed my ability to cope with everything, with living, with my feelings, with my actions and with my decision making,' she says.

Fear and panic attacks

Spiralling alongside anxiety is the emotion of fear—the fear of losing control. It may be the feeling that something terrible is going to happen but we don't know what it is. Or it may be the fear that we are going to be put into a mental hospital or that our children will be taken away from us. Or it may be the fear of not knowing who we really are underneath when we are not on drugs, and how we will cope without our pills. The biggest fear, for some of us, is an accumulation of everything we are afraid of—and the fear that we will be found out. Of course, the fear we experience isn't something that is tangible and real, it's just 'there'. One addict once said to me: 'If I can sum up my withdrawal, it would be fear.'

Vivian describes what fear meant to her. 'There were days when I woke up feeling well, and then suddenly out of nowhere, fear crept up on me. I could never explain what I was afraid of, but it was all-embracing and there was no space left for any other feeling. But I did have this terrible fear that something was going to happen to my child and me. I often wanted to go to school to see if my daughter was all right. It often happened when I was just walking along the street—I suddenly stopped in my tracks and felt the fear come up on me. The people around me started to feel unreal. Noises started to get unbearably loud and the light was too bright. All my senses became stronger—all geared into negative sounds, sights, feelings and perceptions. I didn't breathe properly. I started to feel hot and cold, the palms of my hands began sweating, my knees turned to jelly and I felt dizzy until my legs gave way, almost as if I was fainting. My heart started to race and my thoughts, all negative and morbid, were in a whirlpool. The more I tried to get out of this vicious circle, the more I felt as if I was caught in quicksand. I took more tranquillisers but in the end not even the pills made the fear go away—it got worse and worse. I remember feeling: this is it, neither my mind nor my body will be able to withstand any more of this.'

'Once it was so bad that I just collapsed in my office at work and I couldn't get up. I think it was total exhaustion from the fear. I had gone through a panic attack and that really drained me, it was the mental strain. It also happened in withdrawal, when I was being driven to work in a mini cab. Thoughts raced through my mind: what if the car crashes?; what if I'm run over?' what if I get stuck in traffic?; what if . . . what if . . . and all the whats and ifs were negative. Sometimes when the fear came over me I started to talk incessantly to whoever was close, trying to hang onto a sense of reality. If I was real enough for these people to talk to and they could hear me, then surely that was proof that I really did exist. For the same reason I'd rather have someone right beside me instead of being alone, proving I did still exist and wasn't slowly disintegrating into thin air.'

Margaret describes what fear meant to her: 'Everything had to appear normal, look normal and carry on as normal. I didn't want my family to know how I felt. All I wanted was something to enable me to carry on in what I thought was normality and that was to appear to be normal. I just felt they were going to take my baby away from me.'

As this anxiety increases, it may eventually climax, causing a panic attack. During a panic attack we may feel that we can't breathe and our limbs may shake. But it does not last long—only minutes, even though it may feel as if it is lasting much longer. Unfortunately, once we have had a panic attack, we fear the next one. Of course, this builds up more anxiety in us, releasing more adrenaline, and so we get caught up in a vicious cycle—anxiety and fear leading to a panic attack, a panic attack leading to more anxiety and fear.

Gloria saw her panic attacks as being completely out of control of her body, but not her mind. 'I would be in the supermarket walking down the aisles and looking at the shelves, but I wouldn't be able to see what was on them. I'd run out of the supermarket—I wanted to get out but I couldn't find the door. If someone stopped me at the checkout, I'd go berserk. "I haven't got anything", I'd shout. My breathing was short, in gasps. I had this overwhelming feeling of fear which came to a peak.'

Harry experienced his first panic attack in his car. 'It was during the rush hour. I was driving along in the middle lane, the traffic wasn't too heavy, then suddenly I came to this jam. I just had this terrible panic attack, there sitting in the middle lane. I couldn't stand it, so I got out of the car. I left the car in the middle of the road. I felt I had to get away. I couldn't breathe. I saw houses on the other side of the road and I headed for them. I passed the cars and jumped over the middle barrier. Then I started banging on front doors. A woman answered. "I can't breathe", I said. I pointed to the car. She telephoned for an ambulance. The moment I saw the ambulance I felt normal—I now had someone who could look after me. I was terrified that I couldn't look after myself.'

How to cope with a panic attack (from the Huntingdon Drugs Information Advice Line)

1. *Remember* that the feelings are nothing more than an exaggeration of the normal bodily reactions to stress.

2. *Remember* these feelings are not harmful or dangerous—just unpleasant. Nothing will happen.

3. *Stop* adding to panic with frightening thoughts about what is happening and where it might lead.

4. *Notice* what is really happening in your body right now, not what you fear might happen.

5. *Wait* and give the fear time to pass. Do not fight it or run away from it. Just *accept* it.

6. *Notice* that once you stop adding to these panics with frightening thoughts, the fear starts to fade by itself.

7. *Remember* that the whole point of practice is to learn how to cope with fear without avoiding it. So now is the opportunity to make progress.

8. *Think* about the progress you have made so far, despite all the difficulties. Think how pleased you will be when you succeed this time.

TRANX added another point to this list:

9. *Remember* that it helps to turn negative thoughts into positive ones.

If you can learn to accept panic attacks and recall that each time nothing serious happened to you (after all you did *not* die!), you should find they get fewer and fewer over the months, until they are totally gone.

Depression

When we are addicted to tranquillisers or trying to come off, most of us can end up feeling depressed to a lesser or greater degree. Doctors and psychiatrists now accept that benzodiazepines can cause depression both when we are taking the drug and in withdrawal. This depression is different from a psychiatric depression—one that has not been influenced by drugs. And it mustn't be confused with feeling down-in-the-dumps or just miserable; it is a completely different feeling, as you will read in the case histories below.

As in the case of panic attacks, depression too can lead to a catch-22 situation. The anxiety we experience can lead to depression, and then the depression can bring on anxiety, and so it goes on and on—a never-ending cycle.

I have found there can be three different types of depression experienced by people who are taking tranquillisers or coming off.

Chemically caused depression This depression is totally chemically caused. The addict was not depressed before she went on the drug and she is not depressed when she has come through recovery. She is only depressed on the drug and in acute withdrawal. I suffered from this depression.

Double-load depression This depression may be drug-induced combined with the addict's own underlying depression, so the addict may receive a double load: the underlying depression is worsened by the additional withdrawal depression.

Triggered-off depression The individual's own depression may have been triggered off by the withdrawal syndrome, even though it may have been dormant until then. This depression can go on and on well past the recovery period.

Annette suffers from double-load depression. She has been off tranquillisers for over a year but she is still suffering badly from the illness. Her depression started before she took drugs, but it was not as black as it is now. It seems that the withdrawal symptoms did indeed make the depression worse.

'Depression is almost my whole way of life', Annette begins. 'There is nothing else. I wake up and think "what's the point in going through this, why am I doing this?" I feel so low. I have this feeling of utter pointlessness, utter despair, I can't see an end to it. I have no ability to look ahead or make plans of any type. No matter how hard I try I can't actually make myself do it. It is impossible to control my way of thinking. And it doesn't seem to matter what anybody around me tries to do—whether it is buying something for me or taking me out. Even the weather doesn't affect me. Nothing seems to penetrate my mind, even someone saying "you will get better"— that has no effect on me.

'I'm not depressed about circumstances. I don't live in the present, I live in the past. And it's only the bad things in the past that I think about, the bereavements. I dwell on them. I go over and over the same thing and I don't get anywhere because I'm not actually solving anything. Then the guilt sets in. Somehow I feel responsible about those deaths.

'To make a decision in depression is almost an impossibility because everything is so negative. It doesn't matter which way I look at it—there is only a negative answer, so I find it easier not to make a decision. I just hope that someone else does it for me. I can go round and round, but nothing gets through to me. I'm trapped in this black despondency. I seem to be totally slowed down somehow. To go to work, to get up, to get dressed, thinking about cooking a dinner— really the answer is to sit in my room, with the windows blacked out and the telephone off the hook.

'I don't care how my family copes with me. I haven't got a clue what it's like for them. Depression is a very selfish illness. When it lifts I feel guilty, guilty about the way I've been. So I get depressed again. I can't break the cycle. Rather than doing something about it, I just sink back into it, then I surface, and so it goes on. I've no control over it. That's almost the hardest thing to accept.

'I had post-natal depression when my daughter was born. But that was nothing compared to this. That, in itself, creates depression. When you get a glimpse of what you've gone through. I am far worse now than when I was first put on drugs and I've still got to look at what caused me to go on the drugs in the first place. Those lost years.

'Seeing my children grown up and not remembering them, that creates depression. I looked at my daughter the other day, she's twenty-four years old and it's like I'm just getting to know her.

'Everybody else around me seems very normal. Then the envy comes out—why can't I be like them? Everybody talks about what they are going to do, where they are going on holiday. I don't have the ability to do that. I'm very aware that I am different from every-body, so if anybody pins me down with any plans for the future, I just feel I can't do it, not even a week ahead. I can't even imagine still being here two weeks later. This then brings a reaction of intense anxiety because I feel I am different, and so the whole cycle starts off again.

'Suicidal feelings very much come into that as well—my "normal-ity" compared to other people's. My suicidal feelings are wanting to end depression, rather than wanting to end myself. I just feel that if I took an overdose of tablets I would get some peace of mind. I am not thinking of finishing my life.

'The depression is so bad that when it lifts I can't believe I survived it. It's almost as though I was an onlooker, it wasn't me. I think how did I get through this day, week or month?'

Sally was on tranquillisers for over 25 years. She is a typical example of someone whose depression was caused entirely by her drugs. Sally insists that she was not a depressive person before she took tranquillisers. Now that she is off all mood-altering drugs she admits she can feel down at times, as most people do, but she never enters that black stage of depression. When I asked her what severe depression was like for her, she thought for a long time before she could find the correct words with which to answer. 'I couldn't relate to it', she said finally, 'I couldn't reason with it, it wasn't tangible, it wasn't something I could get hold of. It's not like grieving when someone dies—that's natural, it's understandable. But you can't reason with depression.

'And it's not like being upset, because with that you talk about it and you get over it. But you don't get over your depression. It's too deep, it was everywhere, it was all over my body, my brain—it completely took me over. It was like somebody weighing me down, putting weights on my legs so that I literally couldn't move. The worst time was in the morning. I just wanted to put the sheets over my head. I couldn't even physically get my legs out of bed, they were like lead. I wanted to lie down and cry. I didn't know what I was crying for, I couldn't reason with it. I was so frightened—of myself and of what I might do. But I couldn't talk to anyone, the words wouldn't come out. I didn't know how to express myself. So I had to talk to myself in the mirror. I had to be able to see my mouth move.

'Death was on my mind morning, noon and night. Not killing myself, but the feeling that death brought peace and that was the only way to get out of this terrible trap I was in. How could I go on living being trapped in my brain or within myself? I was desolate and lonely. There was no life, no quality left. Physically I was still in existence, but mentally I was dead.

'The depression would come and go. I wouldn't be able to cope, even with the simple things in life, like looking after the children, dressing them and taking them to school. I always felt weird, never with it. Always on the outside looking in. I always thought, why can everybody conduct their lives, why can they do certain things and why can't I? I didn't care about myself. I didn't wash myself. I didn't eat, I couldn't. All day I would sit with my hands clenched, my knees up, hunched up, like in the embryo position in a mother's womb.'

Margaret is another woman who suffered from depression. She was given mood-altering drugs for her post-natal depression after her first baby. But instead of the drugs 'curing' her, they increased her depression, so, like Annette, she too experienced a 'double load'. Her depression lasted well into her recovery, by which time her children were at senior school.

'I just couldn't work out what was happening to me,' she says. 'No way did I think there was anything wrong with the tablets. I really thought this was me. I was a complete depressive, as I had been told by the doctors, and this was the way I was going to have to live. That was the most depressing thing about it really. I would get incredibly frightened about things. I would go out to the supermarket, I would drive down the road and think "I can't do this" and go home again. I know people say "I can't face it today", but it wasn't that sort of feeling. It was a fear that I couldn't do the job. I felt it was too much. I couldn't get there and find a parking space. I would think "what if I have to reverse in a gap and I've got a big car?" I haven't got the physical energy to cope with that. It wasn't so much going into the big shop, it was the sheer physical effort of doing it. It's like the feeling of walking through mud with wellingtons on—you're pushing and pushing. I felt all the time I was pushing against things. It was physically hard going all the time. I felt I had to get myself together again. I was screwing everything up inside me. I was just falling apart.'

Margaret says 'I really thought this was me'. She had been told by the doctors that she was 'a complete depressive'. This over-emphasis by doctors often can make us more depressed than we are already. We see no hope of getting better. We see ourselves staying in this depressed state for the rest of our lives. That's a very bleak picture. Doctors often like to label us, and they like to feel they are helping us towards a better life by giving us drugs. But I believe that we all have the inner strength to overcome our depression, if we really want to. We all have a basic coping mechanism that enables us to override our depression. This is where TRANX and the medical profession often had different views. The medical profession may tell a person, like Margaret, that she needs drugs to cope with life; TRANX would tell her that she needed to off-load her problems and work through them by going to counselling.

For most of us, the depression should eventually lift over the months of recovery, after we have come off all mood-altering drugs. We should notice that very gradually the intervals between the times of depression become longer and longer until the depression has gone altogether. As with most symptoms in withdrawal, the progress can be very slow and for some of us we may find we are into the second year of recovery before it has gone completely.

'I don't want to live'

Doctors have been foiled again in trying to find a suicide-proof drug. An overdose of benzodiazepines might not kill, but the effect of the drug may certainly cause suicidal feelings, and maybe suicide. In Dr Heather Ashton's study of 50 patients who had taken low-dose prescribed benzodiazepines for an average of 10 years, 20 per cent had taken a drug overdose requiring hospital admission.[26]

We may be given the pills by doctors to relieve our depression and/or anxiety, but instead the pills can make us go further and further into depression and/or anxiety. We may feel physically ill and our impression of ourselves may be at its lowest ebb. We may be riddled with guilt, and we may blame ourselves for everything. Gradually we may believe we cannot exist without the drugs. We may see ourselves in a catch-22 situation. The only way out we may be able to see, in our unstable mind, is to end it all.

Sometimes it is hard to reach tranquilliser addicts who have got this low—it is hard to tell them that their suicidal feelings may not be their own but precipitated by the drugs they are swallowing, especially as the feelings can go on for a long time. These tranquilliser addicts sum up how they felt. Nickie, 22 years old, with a young son and a caring second husband, said: 'I didn't care if the pills killed me—I just wanted to take them. I just wanted to be away from the world I was living in. I just wanted to close my eyes—to block it out.'

Margaret said: 'I couldn't see what I had to offer anybody. I couldn't see what I had to live for. I got to the stage when I felt the children and everybody would be better off if I wasn't here, because at least they wouldn't have to make allowances if I wasn't well or not able to do things. They could start picking up and making a new life. I couldn't see any other way. I never attempted it but I was very close to it indeed.'

Gloria suffered from depression, and her only sanctuary was TRANX where she would spend most of her days. But when it got nearer to five o'clock and she knew she would have to go home, her depression welled up inside her. 'I can remember I was trying to stay longer at TRANX because the depression was so engulfing. It terrified me having to walk out of TRANX and go down the road. Just walking down the road to do a bit of shopping made the depression take hold of me. It was just like somebody pulled a blanket over me and smothered me with it. This went on and on, and towards the end I did seriously contemplate suicide.'

Tom, a pensioner, had a urinary problem. The doctors told him that the only way he could get over this was to relax by taking benzo-diazepines. Tom took the drugs and his complaint went away, but he became very depressed and ill on the benzodiazepines, so he weaned himself off. However, his urinary problem came back. His doctor put him back on the pills and told him he would have to be on them for the rest of his life. Tom did not see this as an option, so he left this note for his wife: 'I can't stand the thought of the "prison". I know I can never get better. Either way we can't be together. I know I can't beat the drug, everyone should know what it has done to us.' He then committed suicide.

I found through my work at TRANX (UK) that addicts and those who have just come off the drugs often threaten and talk of suicide, although at TRANX (UK) we have always believed that the individual's inner strength will come through. By working through the depression, full recovery can be achieved in many cases. However, as recovery can be slow and long-term, some extremely depressed people may have no alternative but to take antidepressants for some time.

Mental confusion—'am I going mad?'

When a tranquilliser addict comes to me for counselling, one of the first questions she usually asks is 'Am I going mad?' My answer is always 'No, it's the drugs that are making you feel the way you do.'

The feelings of going mad cannot be taken lightly, yet so many of us get this feeling very strongly. We know we are not 'normal', and we know that most other people aren't experiencing what we are going through. We feel different, isolated and alone. We feel we are going crazy. Liz sums it up like this: 'I go down the road and I can't wait to get home. I look in shop windows hoping I got dressed that day, thinking "my God, why are people looking at me—did I actually get dressed this morning?" I know I am not right. This goes on for some time, confirming that I must be crazy and I need pills. I get caught up in this dreadful cycle of thoughts where I go further into myself and end up in a psychiatric unit. And all the time I am looking desperately for an answer to my illness.'

We believe we are mentally ill because that is the only answer we have to this mental confusion going on in our head. It explains why we are getting the shakes, headaches, tinnitus, blurred vision, depersonalisation, phobias and all the other symptoms we are experiencing. As one client said, 'My mind feels like a busy road junction.' If we have a history of mental illness in the family, we accept this information willingly: 'No wonder I am going mad, it is in the genes.' We want an explanation, and here we have it. Now we can fit together the jigsaw pieces of ourselves.

It is usually many, many years before we question whether the drugs are the reason why we feel ill. We ironically believe that the drugs are keeping us 'sane', and that without them we would be in a worse state. And our doctor does not help us to believe otherwise when he tells us we need our drugs, or writes in our notes that we are neurotic.

Chemical breakdown

We believe we are heading for a 'mental' breakdown, but I call the condition 'chemical' breakdown. The drugs we are taking are causing our illness—they are giving us the stress-like symptoms and the intolerable anxiety often accompanied by severe depression. In fact, I do not believe anyone need suffer a 'breakdown' whether they are on drugs or not. The cause of a 'mental breakdown' is an accumulation of emotional upheavals. If we could *talk* about our problems and off-load our worries and fears, the feeling of a 'breakdown' need never occur.

By stacking up our emotions we are only delaying the day when we have to deal with them. Eventually the problem has to come to the surface for us to be able to live a normal, happy life. But that can only start happening when we are off all mood-altering drugs, and can recover and face the realities.

Phobias and obsessions

When we suffer anxiety, one of the ways in which we express our state is by having a phobic or obsessional reaction. The most common phobia is agoraphobia (fear of public places), but there are also claustrophobia (fear of enclosed places), hypochondria (fear of being ill), social phobias and flying phobia to name but a few.

Let's take agoraphobia. Agoraphobia is the fear of going into open spaces or public places such as streets, shops, crowds, buses, trains, lifts, escalators or tunnels. We might become paralysed with fear and panic when in a supermarket; we might suddenly leave our trolley full of groceries and rush home, as Gloria did. Or we might panic when on a train or even in a small local shop. Once we have panicked in that situation, we may become frightened that we may panic again—in other words, we panic about the panic. So we decide we won't go out, and the spiral of agoraphobia can set in.

Agoraphobia is largely a woman's disease. Some women suffer from agoraphobia before they are on tranquillisers—it might have been the very reason why the doctor prescribed drugs in the first place, even though the Committee on Safety of Medicines states that benzodiazepines 'should not be used for phobic or obsessional states'. Their agoraphobia may be more intense on the drug and in withdrawal. Agoraphobia may also be experienced by women who didn't have the condition before they went on the drugs. Dr Heather Ashton's study of 50 patients who were prescribed low-dose benzodiazepines for ten years found that 20 per cent had developed incapacitating agoraphobia.[27]

So why can we become agoraphobic when we take tranquillisers and when we are in withdrawal? Quite simply, it's one of the effects tranquillisers have on us. As I have mentioned, tranquillisers can increase our anxiety, and we may suffer from loss of confidence, self-esteem and self-worth. All these character changes feed the phobic condition so that it seems safer to stay at home.

Agoraphobia may also be a condition created or encouraged within the family set-up. It may very well be the outcome of an unhappy relationship. Sometimes, the husband may find his wife's agoraphobia to be to his advantage. He is able to have affairs with other women, knowing that his wife can't find out because she is tucked up at home with her 'illness'. Although he may not outwardly encourage the agoraphobia, he may not try to stop the condition either—it is convenient for him.

June, a married woman, stayed at home for a year when she was on tranquillisers. 'After a while my husband went shopping for me because I used to get panic attacks every time I went into a super-market or store. I couldn't bear going down in a basement. I felt I couldn't get out. I was terrified to go on escalators, loathed lifts. I hated the feeling of being locked in with people in case I passed out or felt ill whilst I was out. It became ridiculous. I had a year in bed and on the bed. It was just a feeling of I didn't want to go out—what's the point?' June not only became addicted to tranquillisers but she became more and more dependent on her husband.

Vivian, a single parent, began to feel agoraphobic when she was taking tranquillisers and became totally agoraphobic when she was in withdrawal. 'I'd get a panic attack if I went outside. I thought something horrible was going to happen. I didn't know what was going to happen but I was terrified of being out there. I think it was the vastness of the sky. I don't know what it was because sometimes I could go out at night. If I needed food I ran out to the little corner shop that was open late. I think I could go out at night because nobody could see me—I wasn't frightened then of making a fool of myself.

'Whilst I was on tranquillisers I was able to get to work in a cab— for months this went on and it was money I could barely afford but it was the only way I could travel. Of course, before each journey I took my pill, then I thought "okay, I can face it now." When I came off tranquillisers I had nothing to help me any more, and I became totally housebound for over two months. I arranged for a babysitter to take my daughter to school and for the greengrocer to deliver my food—luckily I am vegetarian. Then, as I had been off work for such a long time, my boss threatened me with the sack. I felt that some-how I had to get back to work. I had heard about TRANX and in desperation I phoned them in tears. They told me I had to face my fear—that it wouldn't disappear otherwise. They told me to take a cab and not to worry if I had to turn back, but just to think of getting to one more road or one more corner before I told the driver to go back home. The next day, I took their advice. The further the cab travelled away from my home, weaving its way through the heavy London traffic, the more I wanted to be in the safety of my own home. But I repeated to myself, "one more road, one more road". As well as this terror I was feeling almost like a rabbit being let out of a cage, wanting to face things and wanting to be part of life again, but frightened of being part of it. Eventually I arrived at work.'

Vivian's agoraphobia was due to a total lack of self-confidence and self-esteem. That's why she felt she could go out at night in the beginning—she felt people couldn't see her—which is very common in agoraphobia. Often agoraphobia isn't so much a fear of just going out as a fear of meeting people, because of the lack of confidence. She talked of being 'lucky' that she was vegetarian because she could have her fruit and vegetables delivered, but I see this as a disadvantage: if she didn't have her food delivered she would have had to go out. As it was, her boss forced her to go out by threatening her with the sack, so she had to face the big wide world again.

If you suffer from agoraphobia it is best to tackle it at the earliest possible stage. Do not give in to it; face the places you are afraid of as much as possible, rather than trying to avoid them. Not going to the places where you had a panic attack will only make it more difficult for you to return to them later. Don't get caught up in the vicious circle of being afraid of the fear, as that can only lead to a panic attack.

Go back to the place you fear gradually. Each time you return you will probably find it easier. Set targets for yourself—remember how Vivian kept saying to herself 'one more road'.

I know it is difficult, but if you do have a panic attack, don't get frightened and try not to worry. Take deep breaths—you *can* breathe deeply, even though you feel you can't. Try to relax your muscles and let the panic attack pass. Instructions for coping with a panic attack can be found on page 53.

You can also help overcome your fear by trying to visualise the situation in which you feel stressful in the safety of your home. By practising facing the situations you fear, you can help yourself regain your confidence.

Surprisingly, some clients who suffered from agoraphobia found it disappeared when they came to TRANX (UK) for the day. The staff were able to send these women out on errands and it wouldn't bother them. This is because they felt secure in our environment.

Agoraphobia is the main phobic condition tranquilliser addicts suffer from, but there are other obsessional states. Liz had a cleaning obsession. 'My flat was spotlessly clean. Every week I would clean it from top to bottom, the picture rails, everything was cleaned.

Certain things got cleaned every day. I'd vacuum every day, the bathroom was cleaned upside down every day. Just fanatically clean. It got worse during the ten years I was on tranquillisers—it got worse until it was an obsessional behaviour. During that time I had a couple of part-time jobs, but I would be at work thinking I must get home because I hadn't cleaned the bath. It's a terrible anxiety.'

Paul had an obsession about washing himself. 'I would be in the bathroom for about four to five hours. I'd clean my teeth for half an hour, and make sure my hair was just right. Then I'd wash myself ten times in one place.'

And Keith, who had once been a gymnast and a physical training instructor, became a hypochondriac. 'The hypochondria started to develop on the drugs. If I had a pain in my chest I thought it was a heart attack. If I got any twinge or pain, it was always something serious like high blood pressure or cancer. When I got cramp in my legs I thought I had multiple sclerosis. I'd have several physical check-ups which always told me that there was nothing wrong.'

Emotional numbness

'My feelings and my emotions of caring for people, loving people, they were gone. They just didn't exist at all', Gloria admits. We take pills to stop emotional pain but gradually the drug anaesthetises all our feelings. We cannot be happy or sad, we cannot love or hate, we cannot cry or laugh. We are numb. Maira, my daughter, remembers how I was on the drugs. She told me: 'I never saw you cry on the drugs. You did not smile, sing or laugh. You didn't do anything.'

We forget how to cry   My life, during the time I was on tranquillisers and sleeping pills, was a rollercoaster of disasters: my husband beat me, I divorced, I was always short of money and one daughter left home when she was sixteen because of my drug-induced aggression. I did not weep to let out my grief. When a sad or painful event happened, I simply took another pill and buried the emotion.

We forget how to love   The simple act of showing affection to our partner, children and family is no longer within our capabilities. We are so wrapped up in ourselves and in our various 'illnesses' that we simply haven't got time for others. A mother may find she can't show her affection to her children any more. She no longer gives them a cuddle or a kiss, and the words 'I love you' have no meaning, as Vivian discovered. 'Now that I am off tranquillisers and I look at my little girl, I can feel the love I have for her. But when I was on drugs I could neither love nor hate. I could feel nothing.'

Likewise, we may not feel any love for our partner and our sexual desire may become non-existent. Sometimes we may not even like being held or cuddled by our partner. Chola is a young African woman and lives with her husband in Nigeria. When she found it hard to conceive, her doctor gave her tranquillisers. Over the years Chola gradually lost interest in sex. This caused a battle within herself: she knew she should want to have sex with her husband but she had lost her desire for it. 'I tried to have sex with my husband so that he would not complain. It wasn't so much that I worried about him going off with other women because he believes in Christianity and he wouldn't do that. But he'd say, "I'm fed up with you. You are so frigid, you are not responding." Then I worry a bit and I pray to God to help me to respond so that my marriage will not break up.'

When a man loses his sexual desires, he may believe his manhood is threatened which, in turn, can create depression. David was an intelligent and debonair man. He was on tranquillisers for several years, and after some time they caused him to become impotent. He lost his self-esteem and felt he had lost his manhood. This loss was added to a string of symptoms caused by the drugs and so contributed towards his depression. In the end, David committed suicide.

Of course losing our sexual desires isn't always hard on us—we are numb, we can't feel—but for our partner it can be very wounding (see page 124). But we can't blame the pills for every couple who fall out of love. Maybe the emotion of not loving our partner is the correct emotion—maybe our relationship is the very reason why we were prescribed tranquillisers.

We forget how to laugh Comedy television programmes, jokes or funny situations don't even make us smile. We don't react. Betty was prescribed tranquillisers when her son was born, and she doesn't remember laughing again until she was off all mood-altering drugs when he was eighteen years old. 'I used to laugh a lot when I was young', she says, 'but when I started taking those pills I didn't laugh anymore. I don't ever recall laughing. I would sit and watch television with my family and I could never laugh at anything that was on.'

Because we are emotionally numb we have no interest in life. We isolate ourselves. We lose friendships. We simply withdraw ourselves into our shell, believing that our only friend is the little yellow or orange or blue or white pill.

Argumentativeness and aggression

'I would get really heated up about things and my change of mood could be very sudden, even with my daughter. I used to get aggressive sometimes. It would swing very quickly. One minute I was very aggressive and the next minute I felt totally loving. I was totally unbalanced. These mood changes were too much and too rapid—even I couldn't cope with the swings', says Vivian.

Tranquillisers are taken for their calming effects. But paradoxically when taken over a long period of time (more than a few weeks) they can sometimes have the reverse action, as they do with anxiety and insomnia. We may find we become aggressive and more argumentative, in just the same way as some people do if they drink alcohol. This is basically because benzodiazepines affect the brain processes which generate emotional reactions. The drug can't distinguish between one emotion and another, so it influences the emotion of rage just as it does the emotion of anxiety.[28]

An outburst of rage or aggression can also be due to a loss of control. Dr Heather Ashton believes that we are much more aggressive underneath than we appear to be, but we keep this emotion at bay because it is anti-social. But when we are on tranquillisers we are no longer in control of our emotions, so our aggression may suddenly flare up and we have no way of keeping it at bay.

When I was on tranquillisers I became aggressive. It was because of my aggression that I began to suspect the pills were changing my personality. The event that made me stand back and look at myself for the first time in many years was when my youngest daughter, who was nine years old, had been naughty. Instead of just telling her off, I hit her across the leg, but I didn't do it just once—I seemed to go on uncontrollably. When I stopped I realised what I had done, but I knew it wasn't 'me' hitting out. I wasn't an aggressive person. I had lost control because of the pills.

Being out of control can lead to crime. Psychiatrists have found that a lot of the violent crimes we see today are by people who are on tranquillisers. Violent acts such as sexual offences, shoplifting, baby-battering, wife-beating and grandma-bashing have been committed by people on tranquillisers.[31] And Professor M. Rawlins reported that 90 per cent of baby-battering is the result of one parent taking tranquillisers.[29]

Paul, who has been imprisoned for theft, believes that tranquillisers made it easier for him to commit the crimes because they gave him a 'couldn't-care-less' attitude. He didn't think of the consequences. 'I knew it was wrong to steal', he says, 'but I just didn't care. I'd nick cheque books and credit cards while I was on tranquillisers and there would have been no way that I could have walked into a shop and signed somebody else's signature, and had the nerve to stand there, unless I took tranquillisers.'

Not every tranquilliser user becomes aggressive, but many become more argumentative. A small mishap becomes a major drama. The simple accident of a spilt bottle of milk may create an argument that goes on for days. Betty remembers how she used to shout at her children. 'I used to cry and scream and get hysterical. I think it was a cry for help. But then nobody helped me. And every time I went to the doctor he'd say "you need to take some more pills and something stronger".'

Drowsiness

Most people who take tranquillisers suffer from drowsiness. It was one of the first side-effects to be mentioned by doctors as far back as 1960, when one man who was taking Librium fell asleep at the wheel of his car.[30]

It isn't any wonder that we feel fatigued and drowsy. Valium (a long-acting benzodiazepine) can stay inside the body for up to 200 hours. But, of course, we don't just take one Valium, we might take 5mg at 8a.m., 5mg at 2p.m. and 5mg at 8p.m.—so the drug accumulates. Even short-acting benzodiazepines spend between two and twenty hours in the body before they are eliminated. This means that when we are taking tranquillisers and sleeping pills we are never fully alert. This drowsy feeling can slow down our reactions. So of course, driving a car shouldn't even be attempted. But how many people take a sleeping pill at night and then jump into the car the next morning to go to work? And more to the point, how many doctors tell their patients not to drive or use machinery when they hand them the prescription?

Feeling drowsy can be especially dangerous in the elderly. One elderly lady felt so dopey that she fell and broke her hip. June remembers her gait was so unsteady that she had to hold on to the walls and furniture as she walked across the room. 'It took me about an hour to have a bath', says Liz, 'because I was just so slow. I could switch into "slow" and it would last for days—I just couldn't get myself going.' And remember Vivian's cousin, who saw Vivian moving in slow motion as if the film wasn't going at the right speed.

Drowsiness affects the way we talk. Angela began to speak with a slurred speech. 'I was occasionally "dopey" and "not quite there". Friends said that I sounded as if I was speaking from the bottom of a whisky bottle, that I sounded drunk—even though I don't drink. The awful thing was that I didn't realise that my speech was sometimes slurred. I thought I spoke perfectly normally.'

Our mental reactions can slow down, so that we find it hard to comprehend what is being said to us or what is happening to us. 'In the end', says Pam, who was on tranquillisers for fifteen years, 'I didn't feel part of the family. There was a wall around me. I was just on my own and they couldn't get through. They would talk to me but it was as if their mouth was moving and no sound was coming out because I couldn't take anything in.' Not being able to communicate puts a strain on the family as well, as Liz's daughter found out. 'Mum would never understand what I was saying, I would have to repeat it, I would have to find another way for even the simplest things. I would say, "Mum, I am going out, can you pick me up?" I would tell her the time and the place over and over again.'

We are even slow to react to situations. Those close to us may see our behaviour as being cold and without feeling. This happened to me when one of my daughters was sexually attacked on her way home from school. The natural reaction would be one of rage and of wanting to find out who it was. But I didn't react, as my other daughter remembers. 'There was no response. We were talking to a zombie. She would listen but there was no reaction to what had happened or what was being said.'

Exhaustion

Exhaustion usually only happens when we are coming off the drugs. It isn't simply a feeling of being tired: it is an extreme mental and physical fatigue which can go on and on. But although we are utterly exhausted, we may not be able to sleep. This exhaustion may be because we are so wrapped up in learning how to cope with life, and how to deal with our anxiety, and because we are always having doubts about whether we will recover.

Gloria explains what exhaustion was like for her. 'I was walking in the park with a friend. There was a seat and I said, "I must sit down, I can't go on any further." It wasn't because my legs were tired—it was because the whole of me was exhausted. I just felt that if I took one more step I was going to die. But my friend made me get up from the seat. He grabbed hold of me and made me walk. Every step I took I felt I couldn't breathe. I was in a sweat—I was absolutely soaked.'

Memory and concentration

After a period of time on the drugs we may find our memory failing and our concentration going. We may forget to turn up for appointments or meetings with friends. We may begin to forget anniversaries and birthdays. We may forget to turn off the gas to the cooker or the running water for a bath. Again, we very often aren't the first to notice how forgetful we are becoming. Our family and friends may notice, and if they don't realise we are a tranquilliser addict, and that it's the drugs which are making us forgetful, they may regard our behaviour as anti-social and begin to stop making arrangements with us.

Our concentration may begin to falter, which is ironic when you consider that tranquillisers are sometimes given for exam nerves.

Some of us may find that we can't read a newspaper, watch television, or even concentrate on a conversation.

It isn't any wonder our memory fails: benzodiazepines can make us forgetful. Some are used before surgery so that the patient calms down and can't remember the operation. In that instance this amnesic property of benzodiazepines is quite rightly used. But when the drug is taken for a long period of time, not being able to recollect events can be disastrous and heartbreaking. Professor R. G. Priest believes that the amnesic effect may also be dangerous especially in times of crisis when the correct response to a situation is vital. And when it is given for bereavement it may delay the feelings of coming to terms with the sad loss. [31]

Two Danish psychologists, Jensen and Poulson, found that a person on diazepam won't be able to remember things learned while taking the drug—unless they take it again! They believe that if a patient learns how to cope with pressures and how to relax on the drug, she will forget everything she has learned when she stops taking the drug. However, if she takes the drug again her memory will come back. [32]

It isn't until we come off the drugs that we may realise that there is a near total blank in our memory of our pill-taking years. When Betty sits with her family and looks through their photographic album she can't remember the places or the events. When her children say to her, 'Don't you remember, Mum, when . . .', she looks at them blankly. She has no memory. It's as if pages of her photographic album have been ripped out. Of course, she wishes she could have back those years when her children were young and growing up, but they have gone for good—they have become lost years.

Nightmares

When we take benzodiazepines we usually do not dream. When we are coming off, we may experience nightmares. Vivian saw her nightmares as 'all the rubbish in my head coming out.' The nightmares can be morbid thoughts, or they may be frightening and horrific, and in them you may be doing nasty things to yourself or to others. Don't be alarmed or upset over your nightmares; they are normal in withdrawal. Look at them as all the anger suppressed over the years coming out in a distorted fashion. You need to adjust psy-chologically to 'catching up' with previously suppressed feelings.

Margaret remembers: 'Everyone was shouting and yelling at me. I'd wake up. I'd shake and shake. And I'd sweat like mad. My hus-band held me saying "don't worry, you'll be all right." It would go on for an hour or so. And then I'd be too frightened to go back to sleep again.'

But, as with most withdrawal symptoms, nightmares too should pass in time.

Daymares (reliving the past)

Tranquillisers anaesthetise us to events and emotions. So whatever we experience or whatever emotions we are meant to feel when we are taking the drugs, we don't. However, all those events and emotions have been registering in our brain even though we are not aware of it. So when we come off, these emotions surface. They are let loose.

As we didn't live through the emotion or event at the time it hap-pened, we have to go through the feelings when our emotions are ignited again. Unfortunately, it's the sad memories, not the good ones, that surface. It's the bereavements, the frustrations, the injus-tices that have happened during our pill-taking time that are stirred up, and they become as real as if they are happening at that very moment.

There isn't any order or continuity to reliving the past—the memories just emerge with no rhyme or reason. 'There are weeks when I wasn't in the present,' explains Liz. 'I would shoot back into periods of time in my life that I had completely forgotten about when I was on pills. I would start to remember things, periods of my life, little bits of time, and that was really confusing. I didn't know where I was. I wasn't in the present and I wasn't in the past.'

Fear welled up in Diana's daymares. 'It was fear of everything. It was reliving the past—never the good aspects. The thoughts came in an incontinent way. Whatever I did, I couldn't change them. All my emotions and thoughts—everything was overreacting. All just crowded in. My adrenaline was really up. Then when I was in this state I was terrified of the future. Horrid thoughts came into my mind about death and the most negative things that I had ever thought of before. It was very frightening.'

Illusions and hallucinations

Illusions and hallucinations happen in about five per cent of people going through withdrawal.[33] An illusion is when we see a spot on the wall and interpret it as a spider, and an hallucination is when we see something out of nothing. Addicts have told me they've seen snakes, reptiles and weird pictures. These illusions and hallucinations usually only occur if we are wrongly or too quickly withdrawn.

Paranoid feelings

Paranoia is the feeling that people are talking about us behind our backs. Of course, we always believe they are saying bad things about us, never good! We have, after all, lost our confidence and self-esteem, so we feel very vulnerable. As our confidence comes back, so this symptom evaporates.

I suffered from paranoia when I returned to work after being in the Drug Dependency Unit. Whenever I entered the office and saw the staff talking together, I firmly believed they were whispering tales about me. My confidence was so low that I could not envisage that they may just be talking about work or saying something complimentary about me.

Feeling of unreality (derealisation)

We may feel unreal. For some of us this can be the feeling of standing next to our own body or someone looking over our shoulder. However, individuals appear to have different perceptions of this feeling.

Frank suffered from the former type of derealisation. 'I could see myself and I was standing next to me,' he says. 'There were two of me and I was looking at myself. It was weird.'

I suffered from the latter form of derealisation. It happened when I first came off tranquillisers. My boss would be dictating a letter to me, and I would feel as though he was speaking to someone behind me. I felt my soul was standing outside my body, separated from it.

In the end, I would joke about it, saying 'Oh! You're dictating to my ghost.'

Depersonalisation

Quite literally, some of us don't know who we are. We lose our identity. Even if we are in familiar surroundings we don't recognise them. We may have no concept of anything that is going on around us. Tim suffered from depersonalisation when he woke up in the mornings. 'I wouldn't know who I was or where I was. I didn't know what year it was or what address I was at. I used to leave familiar things lying around where I would see them immediately, like my passport, so when I woke up I could look at my passport and that would reassure me and tell me who I was.'

Other psychological symptoms

There are many other psychological symptoms, but the main point is to accept them as part of the road to recovery. Eventually they should all pass. The symptoms can include: craving for more drugs, agitation and restlessness, dejection—'What's the point of going on?', lack of co-ordination and difficulty in making decisions and plans.

Now we look at the physical symptoms.

Insomnia

Another paradoxical side-effect and withdrawal symptom is insomnia. Many of us start taking benzodiazepines because we can't sleep, but the sleeping pills will only induce sleep for a short period of time—just a few days, then their effect wears off. In other words, we become tolerant to the drug. This may develop to the point where the pill has no effect on us at all, and so we may be suffering insomnia whilst we are taking sleeping pills. Yet again, benzodiazepines have created the very problem for which they have been prescribed. Sometimes doctors who are unfamiliar with a patient reaching the tolerance level believe, quite wrongly, that the original problem is coming back, and they prescribe more or stronger pills.

Ironically, insomnia can be created during a stay in hospital. If a patient has been prescribed sleeping pills routinely for a few days, she may suffer from a rebound effect of not sleeping when she stops taking the pills when she goes home. Of course, when this happens she immediately remembers the sleeping pills which helped her to sleep during her time in hospital. And so the spiral of addiction can take off. Her GP will be informed by the hospital that sleeping pills were given, so he will be happy to prescribe them.

Even if we did sleep well on the drugs, insomnia can still be severe in withdrawal. The symptom not only occurs in people who have been taking sleeping pills, but also in people who have taken tran-quillisers—remember, they are similar drugs. It isn't surprising that we suffer from insomnia in withdrawal because, as explained on page 22, when we are taking benzodiazepines they are not inducing a natural sleep. In recovery, our body and mind have to relearn how to sleep.

Maybe lack of sleep is one of the hardest withdrawals to cope with. So many people say to me, 'If only I had a night's sleep I wouldn't feel so bad.' The night and lying in bed becomes some-thing they fear. The bed is no longer seen as somewhere to rest their weary bodies, but as a battle-ground of wanting to sleep and not being able to.

The best way to treat insomnia in withdrawal is to accept it as a symptom. Don't watch the clock seeing the hours tick away in the dark stillness of your room. Read a book (if you can), listen to soo-thing music (if you aren't on your own, wear headphones), or get up and do something. If the bed has become a place you hate, rest on the sofa. Gradually your sleep should return, but it may take some time. As with all symptoms, you should see a slow improvement over the months.

Annette suffered from insomnia during withdrawal. 'The worst thing about insomnia,' she says, 'is not being able to turn your mind off. My mind was constantly thinking odd thoughts all day and then at night it would be the same thing. It was like a constant drilling that went on and on and on. I actually didn't feel tired either physically or mentally. Half the time I did not even bother to go to bed. I was too hyperactive to feel tired. I could clean my house in the middle of the night from top to bottom. I used to bake cakes and wash floors. It was as though I had years of excess energy in me. It was all racing around and I didn't quite know what to do with it all. I actually didn't feel tired for a long, long time.'

'Nothing could have helped me at the time with my insomnia. I had no control over my body or mind. I tried everything, like having a bath, reading, not drinking coffee or tea or anything that might stimulate me. I used to go to my children's bedroom and sit on the edge of their beds, watching them sleep and thinking they don't know how lucky they are to have this ability to just go to sleep. It struck me as amazing, at the time, that they could just lie there for eight hours or so, which was something I could not do.'

I also suffered from insomnia. When I told my doctor I couldn't sleep and yet I was taking my pills, she simply replied, 'take more pills'. Eventually, I reached the stage where I was taking a pill every half-an-hour throughout the night—and still I did not sleep. Insomnia became one of my more acute withdrawal symptoms when I was coming off. It lasted for many months, but sleep did return eventually. Today, I sleep eight to nine hours every night, without pills!

The shakes

'I would be standing on the train reading a newspaper,' says Frank, 'then all of a sudden from my head to my toes I would shake. People started to look at me, thinking "what the hell is wrong with that man?" It's nothing—just what's being pumped down me.'

Shaking uncontrollably, tremors, tics, muscle jerking and muscle tension is experienced by most of us who are on or are coming off benzodiazepines. I feel we have to accept this symptom as part of withdrawal, knowing that it should go in time. I agree it can be distressing. It isn't pleasant to find that you are shaking so furiously you are unable to pour a cup of tea. And it might be embarrassing when muscles suddenly jerk when you are sitting in a crowded room, but always remember that it isn't you: it's the drugs.

GPs may be quick to prescribe more drugs, such as beta-blockers, to cure the problem. These drugs can have sedating properties and are able to stop the shaking. Dr Heather Ashton has found in her clinic that in some extreme and embarrassing cases it has stopped her patients from severe shaking and helped them over the 'hump' of withdrawal. But I disagree with this kind of treatment. Any drug taken which has sedating properties can only delay the full recovery process. Although the shakes may be less severe, the recovery process may be lengthened. And who says beta-blockers are not dependence forming—the doctors? (See page 191.)

Unsteadiness and vertigo

We may say that the floor seems to move or that we don't feel in contact with the ground. We may experience a feeling of imbalance, unsteadiness, dizziness in our head, giddiness, 'swimminess' or, in its most chronic form, vertigo. Dr David Marjot points out that although these symptoms 'seem to be a common feature of benzodiazepine withdrawal, they are symptoms which are reported in anxiety, though not always to the same intensity as in benzodiazepine withdrawal.'

Audrey, 58 years old, had always been vulnerable to giddy spells, but during the fifteen years of taking tranquillisers she also experienced dizziness, 'swimminess' and vertigo. 'I felt drunk,' she explains. 'The floor moved when I went to walk. I felt very unsteady. Throughout the whole time I was on tranquillisers I always felt the floor was moving. I used to feel if I turned round quickly, I'd fall over. It got ten times worse when I was coming off and a hundred times worse when I stopped completely.'

It came to a peak when she was a few weeks off tranquillisers. 'That night I went to bed feeling all right. In the middle of the night I woke up feeling dizzy. I tried to get to the end of the bed but everything was going round and round. I tried to get to the bathroom with my husband's help and I completely lost my balance. I didn't know where I was, whether I was standing up or sitting down. The sickness was horrendous. The curtains were moving and the walls were swinging away from me. I couldn't make my eyes stay put, I couldn't look at anything because it's like being cross-eyed. It all moved away from me.'

These attacks of vertigo can happen at any time, without warning.

I suffered one in the middle of a large department store—all of a sudden the walls seemed as if they were collapsing on me. Dr David Marjot suggests that when an attack happens, the most important thing is to try to distract your attention from it. Learning new skills or doing sports, like yoga or badminton, will help override the symptoms by giving you new feelings. Also, by learning new skills you will boost your confidence and self-esteem. In time, most ex-tranquilliser users get over this imbalance.

Hypersensitivity to all sensations

We can become hypersensitive to sounds, light, touch and smell. The least stimuli can set off our senses. The gentle tick of a clock or the door bell ringing can sound like Big Ben, ordinary daylight can become harsh, a gentle brush against our arm may feel like a punch, and smell can become overpowering. Hypersensitivity may become more acute in withdrawal because, as we have seen, there is nothing to dampen down our sensations: we no longer have our pills, and our own coping mechanism is in repair.

I was affected by noise both when I was on tranquillisers and when I was coming off. This in turn affected my children, who weren't allowed to have the television or radio on loud. Maira, my eldest daughter, remembers what happened. 'We would be watching television in the front room, and Mum would be in the back room. But any noise and she would go crazy. So we'd have to have the television on so low we could hardly hear it. We couldn't have friends around either because of the noise. But we learnt to accept it. We learnt to understand that when we came home from school we had to be quiet and could not jump around. We literally had to sit down and do something, and we could not be boisterous in any way.'

Vivian wore sunglasses indoors even though her flat was quite dark, but she remembers 'the light seemed so bright it would hurt my eyes.' Margaret became sensitive to touch. 'Someone would just have to brush past me and I would feel as if they had bruised me,' she explains. And Amanda, who lived above a restaurant, had to move home because she found the smell of the cooking too nauseating and overpowering. Before she went on drugs, the wafts of aroma didn't bother her at all.

Whistling in the ears (tinnitus)

This can be fairly common. It may occur while we are still taking the drugs and when we are coming off. It has been said that it may initially result from our general hypersensitivity.[34] For some, it may last for some time during recovery.

Vivian started to suffer from tinnitus when she was taking tranquillisers. It became so acute she was admitted to hospital. On her arrival she told the doctors she was taking tranquillisers but they did not associate her condition with the side-effect or withdrawal of the drug, and wrongly diagnosed her as having suspected Ménière's disease, for which she was given more drugs which were ineffective.

If the tinnitus keeps you awake at night, try putting a radio or tape recorder on, preferably one which will switch itself off after a given length of time, and set it just loud enough to drown the sound in your head or ear. This can also help if you cannot 'switch off' your brain when you go to bed.

Pain in jaw and face (oro–facial discomfort)

This is fairly common. It feels as if you have an extremely bad toothache. Have your teeth checked but be aware that it could be withdrawal. Our gums can be one of the first parts of our body to be affected, so many tranquilliser addicts have had their teeth pulled out unnecessarily, as after the teeth have been extracted the pain still persists. Even people with dentures suffer from this 'toothache'!

Try to avoid taking painkillers if you can: some may have narcotics in them. Generally they are ineffective for withdrawal symptoms and may actually delay your recovery.

Pains in the limbs, back, neck and shoulders

Diana cried in agony over the pain in her neck which eventually spread over her shoulders and down her spine. What she didn't realise at the time was that she had reached her tolerance level to the tranquillisers and that she was experiencing withdrawal tension, not arthritis or rheumatism as the doctor had suggested.

Towards the end of my addiction I had been told by the medical profession that my spine was rotting away. I couldn't twist, turn or bend. I had to make my bed on my knees. For over two years I went to the hospital for heat treatment, which had no effect. Once I came off benzodiazepines my spine was perfect.

Here we see again a withdrawal symptom creating the opposite desired effect. Benzodiazepines are given as a muscle relaxant, yet they take away our own muscle coping mechanism. When we first take benzodiazepines, the drug relaxes our muscles. But gradually, over a period of time, our body may begin to rely more heavily on the drug to carry out the job of relaxing our muscles, instead of using its own natural mechanism. The muscles become dependent on the drug. When this happens, or when we stop taking the drug altogether, our muscles can go stiff because we have neither the drug nor our own muscle relaxant to stop them from doing otherwise.[35]

To get some relief from throbbing or painful legs, sit or lie down with your legs raised slightly above your body. You can rest your legs on a chair if you're sitting, or a pillow if you're lying down.

Stomach problems

Many addicts have suffered from gastroenteritis, both when they are taking the drugs and when they are coming off. Diarrhoea, constipation, colicky pains, nausea and vomiting can become quite acute, so much so that we may be under hospital observation or even undergo an operation. Dr Heather Ashton found in her study that eighteen per cent of patients had undergone extensive gastroenterological investigations (mostly diagnosed as irritable bowel).[36] Not surprisingly, once we are off benzodiazepines our stomach complaints usually start clearing up.

Liz saw the physical withdrawal symptoms of diarrhoea as the complete loss of her dignity of being a human being. 'It was awful. I began to feel like an animal. I just felt horrible about myself. I remember my cat watching me one day—I was crawling on the floor on the landing to get to the telephone. I looked at him and thought "If this was you, we would have you put down."'

Keith developed a very large ulcer whilst he was on tranquillisers because of his increased anxiety. When he came off all his mood-altering drugs and returned to the hospital to get it checked, the ulcer had healed up.

Although stomach complaints may be due to withdrawal, you may be able to ease the misery a little. Don't dose constipation as it can suddenly change to the reverse, and then you will be in trouble! Eat a sensible diet with plenty of fresh vegetables and a high fibre content. Take plenty of fluids and exercise. With diarrhoea, let it burn itself out. A diet of dry toast and water may help. Stay clear of milk, cheese and yoghurt as these can feed the diarrhoea. Stomach pains, acidity and indigestion can be due to the lining of our stomach becoming irritated in withdrawal. Your best remedy here is to protect the stomach from damage from excess acid by drinking cold milk or a magnesium trisilicate liquid.

We may also complain of food allergies or food intolerance, but when tests are carried out they almost always give a negative result and the condition does not respond to conventional treatment. Very often, when we encounter a problem like this, we turn to alternative or 'fringe' medicine, or we try various types of diets. We may even be convinced we have intestinal candidiasis or damage to our immune system. But, of course, we don't—it's just another symptom.[37]

Weight changes

Our weight can change during withdrawal syndrome. Some lose and some gain. Frank, who normally weighs ten stone, went down to eight stone, and Liz lost so much weight she was under hospital observation. However, I have found that it is antidepressants which mainly cause an increase in weight.

When I was coming off my mood-altering drugs I went down from eleven to ten stone. But once off, my weight soared to thirteen stone. This was basically because I binged on sweets and chocolates, which I realise now was probably due to a drop in my sugar level, and the need to put something in my mouth instead of the drugs. Eventually, my eating habits returned to normal and so did my weight.

Urinary problems

It is very common to suffer from incontinence or frequency. I suffered from this complaint in the Drug Dependency Unit and although it was embarrassing at the time, I did get better!

Hormone problems

Benzodiazepines actually work on the hormones, so it isn't any wonder that they can go out of control. Women often complain of heavy periods, changes in the menstrual pattern, vaginal discharge and a burning sensation in the vulva. Our breasts can become tender and begin lactating. It was once reported a woman started lactation sixteen years after her last pregnancy.[38]

If you do have a problem with the skin around the vagina becoming very dry, a light application of Vaseline may provide a barrier so that the urine does not sting. The application of a little Acriflex every now and then may promote healing if there are weeping cracks as well. Bathing with a saline solution can be soothing and healing.

Pre-menstrual tension (PMT) can go sky high when we are taking the drugs and coming off. The same symptoms can also occur in withdrawal, so when we are going through withdrawal and suffering from PMT we are getting a 'double load' of these symptoms. The following list gives the symptoms which can occur in PMT.

depression	swollen joints
weepiness	fatigue
irritability	aggression
mood changes	suicidal tendencies
bloatedness (water retention)	craving for food (sugar)
headaches	bad vision
backache	

In the menopause we encounter a similar situation where the symptoms of the 'change of life' are similar to those of withdrawal. So we are again receiving a 'double load' of the same symptoms. These are the symptoms of menopause:

headaches	anxiety
giddiness	depression
tingling hands and feet	palpitations
flushing	

Doctors can be rather enthusiastic about prescribing hormone tablets, but some of these may contain meprobamate, a minor tranquilliser. I believe it is best to try to cope with these symptoms as they occur, whether they are due to withdrawal or to the menopause.

The hormone problem isn't just a woman's problem. Men can also suffer with swollen tender breasts and slight discharge, impotence, loss of seminal fluid and pain in the testicles.[39]

Palpitations

June had pills for palpitations when she was taking tranquillisers. Now she is off and no longer needs them, her heart is fine.

Both young and old may experience palpitations, pains and a tightness in the chest. It isn't any wonder that we do, as Shirley Trickett points out in her book *Coming Off Tranquillisers and Sleeping Pills*. 'If you were running for a bus and your heart rate increased, it wouldn't worry you. Because you are cutting down on drugs that have slowed the heart rate, you can expect a similar effect.'[40]

However, although your symptoms are probably due to withdrawal, if you are worried, do consult your doctor. Unfortunately, he may prescribe beta-blockers, which are normally given to reduce heart-rate and lower blood pressure. He may tell you that beta-blockers are non-addictive, but be wary: tranquillisers were once thought of as non-addictive! The effects of beta-blockers are described on page 191.

Overbreathing (hyperventilation)

Because we are suffering from over-anxiety, some of us may have difficulty in breathing, or we may hyperventilate and gasp for breath. We must always remember that we *can* breathe! (See page 169 for breathing techniques.)

The first time I met June was at a group meeting at TRANX (UK). She was unable to talk. Her breathing was so gasping that her husband had to speak for her, and when she asked me a question she had to write it down. She sat in the room with twenty other addicts and their partners, breathing in short gasps but listening intently. However, it wasn't anything that was said at the meeting that made her realise that her condition was because of the pills she was swallowing—her confirmation came from another woman who had the same breathing difficulties. By the end of the evening just being able to identify with someone reduced her anxiety and her breathing problem eased a little.

Headaches

Withdrawal headaches are unlike an ordinary headache. Most people coming off tranquillisers suffer from this; it can either be the feeling of a tight band around the head or a heavy brick resting on top of your scalp. Unfortunately, the headaches can be very persistent. Chola describes them as 'like a pin inside my head, and a strong band tied tight around my scalp. Then my teeth shudder like when you knock on metal—it's that vibration.'

Blurred vision

We are not going blind, and our eyesight is not getting worse. Some of us have gone to the optician because we feel we need either spectacles or stronger ones. This has been found to be a waste of time and money because our eyesight should return to its original state when we are off our mood-altering drugs.

Flu-like symptoms

Sore throat, stuffy nose and sinus problems can affect many addicts. It isn't always the common cold or the flu, but just another withdrawal symptom. However, we can be more prone to catching colds and flu because our immunity is so low.

Other physical symptoms

There are many other physical side-effects and withdrawal symptoms. Some of them are: tingling in the hands and feet ('pins and needles'), skin rash and itching, difficulty in swallowing, sore tongue, excessive saliva, clenching teeth, metallic taste, dry cough, hot and cold shivers, swelling of abdomen, hands, face and feet, hair loss, and cracked lips and mouth corners.

Even though benzodiazepines have now been on the market for three decades, there are still question marks hanging over many of the reasons for the side-effects and withdrawal symptoms. Scientists and doctors are continually putting forward their hypotheses, but as Dr Heather Ashton admits: 'there are still many puzzling features of benzodiazepine withdrawal and the benzodiazepine story remains unfinished.'[41]

Although we may not know why certain symptoms occur, we do know that most symptoms should slowly disappear during the recovery period. Nonetheless, we are all inclined to think that we are the exception, and that we are really sick: 'It just cannot be withdrawal any more—I am different, this must be "me"!' In the end we should be able to enjoy a healthy, happy and normal life. The process of recovery is discussed in Part Three.

CREATING OTHER ILLNESSES

'Over the past thirty years or more (while my wife has been on benzodiazepines) my life has been mostly spent with my wife in doctors' surgeries, waiting rooms and hospitals trying to find out what was wrong with her,' explains John, June's husband.

Withdrawal is a severe illness. But the crying shame is that when we are suffering we often do not realise for a long time that our physical and mental pain is caused by the drugs we are swallowing. Instead we search aimlessly for the cause, and, of course, we fear the worst—that we have cancer, multiple sclerosis, arthritis or some other dreadful disease.

Usually, when we go to the hospital to have tests, the results come out negative. June had tests for water retention, constipation, heart problems and other ailments. 'I was in and out of hospital, testing for this and that. No result came from it. Eventually I did stay in hospital because I was feeling so ill. For six weeks they did tests, they were exhaustive and it was horrible . . . they took a lump out of my stomach and a lump out of my leg to test my muscles. In the end, the doctors just said: "We can't understand it".'

As we are suffering from an 'illness' doctors may prescribe more and more drugs to alleviate the side-effects of pills given previously. As you have read, June ended up on nineteen different pills a day. On top of her benzodiazepines and antidepressants she had pills for her heart, stomach and water retention. Since June has come off of all her mood-altering drugs she doesn't take any pills, except for the odd painkiller. As all her ailments have cleared up she hasn't needed to have any tests, let alone operations!

Keith was another tranquilliser addict who was in and out of hospital and his doctor's surgery with either real complaints or ones that were created by his hypochondria. Once he was off tranquillisers his ulcer and his hypochondria cleared up.

Some of us give up on conventional medicine and turn our hopes to fringe medicine—osteopathy, homoeopathy, acupuncture and other treatments. From my experience, these are often found to be unsuccessful for the purposes of withdrawal. Nor do I believe that we should give up one set of pills only to turn to others, be they homoeopathic, herbal or conventional. We should instead rely on our own inner strength—not pills, of whatever kind—to achieve recovery.

Other therapies such as counselling, psychotherapy and analysis are also often considered. Although I am firmly in favour of talking about our problems and 'off-loading', and I believe they can help us at all stages of recovery, I have nevertheless found that even these therapies cannot be fully beneficial to us while we are on mood-altering drugs. The therapist should understand that our emotions are 'blocked', and so the treatment may not be as effective. It is best to wait until we are off all our pills and our mental confusion has simmered down before we consider in-depth therapy.

Addicts have spent thousands of pounds trying to find the cause of their illness. One addict had to sell her house to pay for her check-ups and operations! Of course, it was all in vain—all her complaints cleared up as her recovery progressed. The NHS has spent millions of pounds on trying to find the causes of these mysterious illnesses. Sought-after hospital beds have been taken up and expensive operations have been performed, when the cause of the illness was often the little yellow, red, white or blue pill: the pill the doctor gave in the first place.

ACCIDENTS ON TRANQUILLISERS

When we take benzodiazepines we are more at risk of having an accident, which isn't surprising when the adverse reactions of the drug may cause drowsiness, light-headedness, lack of co-ordination, confusion and vertigo, and our judgement and dexterity may be impaired. This increases our chances of having a car accident. 'I took tranquillisers to keep calm,' says Angela, 'but not a year passed that I didn't have some kind of motor accident. I wrote one car off, I had dents in the other cars. After I stopped taking tranquillisers, I realised the mistakes I had been making when I was on the drugs. I was careless. I used to throw the car around. My judgement was impaired.'

Many tranquilliser addicts do end up leaving their car in the garage because they realise they aren't capable of driving safely. But some carry on driving irrespective of how they feel as it is the only means of getting around, and in cases of agoraphobia the car often becomes an extension of their home.

Accidents can also happen because we have become so weak. June remembers the time when she decided to leave the house for the first time having been house-bound and virtually bed-bound for a year. 'One day I decided the best thing I could do was to go to Harrods. I was determined to go. My husband agreed to take me. As you can imagine, I was pretty weak. As I stepped out of the taxi outside Harrods, I fell down and I broke my foot. I didn't even get in to the store. I was sent to hospital in an ambulance.'

I AM GUILTY

We may carry feelings of guilt around with us, day in and day out. Some of our guilty feelings may go back to our past or to our childhood. Our wish to bury these feelings might be the very reason we went on drugs in the first place. Again, these feelings of guilt need to be talked through and will have to be dealt with when we are off all mood-altering drugs and start recovery.

But the feelings of guilt I want to discuss here are a direct result of taking the drugs. Even if we didn't have guilty feelings before taking the drugs, during the pill-taking years we may experience some, if not all, of these guilty feelings.

Guilty of being on the pills

Although the little yellow, white, blue and pink pills are often seen by us as our 'friend', we know every time we swallow the pill that we shouldn't be taking it. We feel guilty we have to rely on something to make us function. We feel guilty we need the pill to get us to work, to the shops, to a meeting, to the dentist, to the children's school play. We might know deep down that we are not an ill person, that we should be able to do these things without the aid of a drug. But we have found ourselves caught in a trap; if we don't take the pill we may feel extremely ill, and yet we don't feel well while taking the drug.

Guilty of hiding the addiction

We are terrified of being found out. We may not be able to admit our dependence to our friends or relatives, and in some cases even to our close family, and it is very unlikely that we will tell our boss, in case it backfires on us. We may become ashamed because we don't want to admit to our failure and weakness.

But we may feel guilty that we have to keep this secret from the rest of the world—that we can't be honest and straight. Lying might become a way of life and a means of survival to us. We may tell lies about why we feel ill, why we can't do things and why we can't go to places. All of our lies are to protect our addiction.

Throughout Daniel's university life he kept his addiction to benzodiazepines a secret. He led an isolated university life, not wanting to have close relationships with male students and not wanting to have a love affair with a girl student. He felt that if he became close to anyone, they might find out about his addiction. He felt he could never invite anyone back to his digs in case they opened his bathroom cabinet and saw his bottles of pills. Daniel felt so guilty about his dependence that he wouldn't even admit it to his sister. When she asked him to go to Greece with her, he declined because he didn't know how to hide his bottles of pills in his suitcase. He was terrified that she would find out. By trying to hide his addiction all the time, he got 'very hung up about it', which led to more anxiety and depression.

Guilty of taking more pills than prescribed

We may pretend to ourselves and to those around us that we are taking the prescribed amount of pills, while we are in fact taking more. We may have some stashed away in our car, cupboard or handbag, or hidden in a secret place for when we need an extra boost. To obtain extra pills we may go to another doctor, and lie about being out of our area. Then we may feel guilty about telling yet another lie.

Most tranquilliser users end up taking more pills than prescribed. We know we shouldn't take more, but we can't help ourselves. We need those pills. We have reached our tolerance level. Remember, we are addicts with a small 'a' (see page 40).

Guilty of losing self-respect and confidence

We find it hard to look back at ourselves when we weren't on tranquillisers. 'Why am I not how I used to be? Why don't I laugh, care for myself and others? Why can't I do my job? Why have I let this happen to me? Why have I reached these depths of desperation?'

We may feel guilty that our life has been ruined, that we aren't the person we were before we started taking tranquillisers. We may feel guilty that we don't know how it happened. 'I felt a failure as a man,' says Keith. 'I was a PT instructor. I was in the British Army Royal

Gymnastic team. I've done parachute jumping. When I was young I wasn't frightened of anything and I was as fit as a fiddle. Now I'm terrified of so many things. For me it's so degrading to have to go through withdrawal.' Many men, like Keith, see their manhood threatened.

The responsibility of being a provider, which men expect as husbands and fathers, is taken away from them. They may feel guilty that they have dragged their family down with them, maybe losing their business and their home. This happened to Harry. 'I was once a proud person, telling twenty to twenty-five people what to do. Then seven months later I'm sitting in a drug addiction unit being told to be quiet and make a cup of tea. That's a hell of a change in seven months. That's the indignity I had to suffer, from one extreme to another. From being the boss to being the "dog". People can't change overnight—you get used to a way of life. It really hurts when you go to another way of life so suddenly. It doesn't do anything for your confidence. Losing all that money, losing everything I had, then losing my self-respect.'

Guilty of 'having everything' and still feeling depressed

'Can't think why she's depressed. Look at her—she's got a lovely husband, gorgeous children and that house cost a small fortune.'

For an onlooker it may be difficult to comprehend why a person who has most of the luxuries in life would be depressed. It is much easier for them to understand why single parents, the unemployed or the homeless are on drugs. These people have tangible reasons for their depression. But 'having everything' doesn't necessarily bring happiness. You only have to read about the lives of the rich and famous to realise that money isn't the key to all the good things in life. Many rich and famous people are actually on tranquillisers.

Knowing that you 'have everything' and also feeling depressed can breed the feelings of guilt. Then these guilty feelings may turn into a deeper depression. Remember Margaret, who felt she had everything. 'On the face of it, it looked as if I had everything anyone could want, that's why I found it so difficult to find out why I was depressed. Financially we were well off, I had a beautiful baby and a big house.' Margaret's depression started when she had to give up work to look after her baby. She became lonely. She felt her mind wasn't being stretched by looking after her child. She felt she ought to be happy because she had a beautiful baby. Depression and guilt formed a vicious circle: she felt guilty because she was depressed, and depressed because she felt guilty.

Guilty of not being able to carry out our role

We all have roles to play in society—as mothers, fathers, providers, husbands, wives, lovers, sons or daughters. The roles are clearly defined, and we know what is expected of us. But when we are hooked on tranquillisers we cannot always carry out our roles. A mother might know she has to get the children's lunchbox ready for school, but she can't. A father knows he should support his family financially, but he is afraid of going to work, or he cannot use public transport any more to get to his job.

 We may feel we are letting down the rest of our family, and maybe we realise that because of our addiction the rest of the family is suffering too. But we are not quite sure how to get out of the situation. Suzanne, a mother of two, became agoraphobic on tranquillisers. Because she couldn't go out, her family couldn't go on holiday or outings, and she couldn't go to her children's events at school. Suzanne's agoraphobia didn't just stop her 'life', it affected her husband's and children's lives too. Like Harry when he lost his business, she felt guilty that she was depriving the rest of her family, and so became more and more depressed.

TRANQUILLISERS CAUSING OTHER DEPENDENCIES

I have found through counselling and at TRANX (UK) that when we become hooked on benzodiazepines, some of us may become dependent on many other people. Firstly, we may become dependent on our doctor. Our GP might have been the doctor who first prescribed tranquillisers. Gradually we realise that we cannot survive without our prescription. Although we may question our doctor if he changes the drugs or ups the dose, we don't object even if we don't really agree, because we have lost our confidence, self-assertiveness and self-esteem. We have become putty in our doctor's hands.

We may become dependent on our spouse. During our pill-taking time, we may end up as the subordinate partner. Keith's wife admits that during the years Keith was on pills she became the bossy one. 'I'm the one who wears the trousers,' she says. 'It wasn't a case of wanting to, it was a case of necessity.' Harry's wife was in a similar situation—she had to rush to open the mail in the morning so that she could protect Harry from any letters she knew would upset him.

Because we have no self-worth, nothing matters to us. We won't stand up for ourselves and we may become docile. One addict's husband asked her to stay in to answer the phone even though they had an answering machine. Of course she did as he wanted, even though she had planned to go out. When she was off drugs and her husband asked her again, she refused.

We may become dependent on our family. Again we may become the subordinate member. Our children might like mum or dad on drugs because it 'shuts her/him up', and they are able to get on with their own lives. When we are on drugs we don't moan, because if we get anxious or are unhappy about a situation, we simply take another pill.

As you can see, we might, as tranquilliser addicts, believe we are living in a cocoon with our pills. But that is not so. Our addiction has a knock-on effect in which the lives of every member of our family may be affected, as well as the lives of those around us. How our addiction can change the lives of the ones we love will be discussed in Part Four.

PART THREE

MOTIVATION

I

DO YOU REALLY WANT TO BE FREE OF TRANQUILLISERS?

'Cutting down is a ritual. It's magic. It's terribly powerful. As I filed down the pill, I'd watch every speck because that's the anti-addiction. That's a conscience process.'

Liz

You, and you alone, have to make the decision to come off tranquillisers. No one can decide for you. No one can stop you taking your pills—not your doctor, partner, parent, child or friend. The only way you can achieve full recovery is if *you* decide to come off slowly and stay off *all* mood-altering drugs.

You might say, 'I can stop taking my pills tomorrow if I want to.' But can you? If you have been taking tranquillisers or sleeping pills longer than a couple of weeks it is possible that you may be dependent on them. Or you may believe that you really do need your pills. You may feel that *your* anguish is greater than anyone else's; you may say, 'it's all right for other people to give up tranquillisers, they haven't got *my* problems'. When we are on drugs, we may become consumed by our own ailments. Our problems appear to be greater, our depression appears to be blacker and our insomnia appears to be more acute. We can become self-obsessed and selfish.

You may have tried to come off your tranquillisers in the past, by stopping abruptly—in other words, 'cold turkey'. It may have happened when you suddenly realised you were dependent on the drugs. In a panic, you may have flushed away your pills down the toilet, thinking, 'I'm not going to take those again.' But the next day you nay have found yourself ill with symptoms like sickness, sweating, shaking and blurred vision. Unknowingly you have put yourself into acute withdrawal. Terrified of what was happening to you, you most probably crawled back to your doctor to get another prescription of tranquillisers and/or sleeping pills.

Doctors too have taken patients off benzodiazepines 'cold turkey'. In the past it was through ignorance, but since January 1988 when the Committee on Safety of Medicines published their report of risks of addiction, some doctors have now become concerned about possible legal action. At the end of 1990, the first legal cases were brought before the courts by tranquilliser addicts suing their doctor and/or the pharmaceutical industry.

Fear of your own feelings, of who you really are underneath, could be one reason for you to be hesitant about coming off your mood-altering drugs. Feelings of anger and guilt, which in some cases could go back as far as your childhood, may have been buried during your time on pills. You may feel that to face these feelings will be too painful. This may be especially so if you were given tranquillisers after a bereavement. But by facing up to your feelings, coming to terms with them and accepting them for what they are, you will be able to learn to conquer them.

Let's face it, tranquillisers have been our 'crutch'. You might have called them your 'little friends'. They've been there for when life gets stressful and when problems arise. Think of all the times you've reached for your pills when something unexpected has happened and you felt you couldn't cope. Swallowing a pill has seemingly made your problem vanish, or at least not appear as bad as it is. Without them you will have to face life's ups and downs in the raw. You may feel that if you take away your tranquillisers, you are taking away your life support. But it is so much better to learn how to cope with stress than to bury it.

You might also not want to stop taking tranquillisers because you are frightened of going back to how you were before you went on the drugs. Anxiety, depression, insomnia or agoraphobia may have been the reason why you were prescribed mood-altering drugs in the first place. You may feel that if you stop taking your pills you may suffer from that condition again. And at times, you may very well have thought that you had a relapse into your pre-benzodiazepine condition.

Staying on tranquillisers may not be just down to you: your partner

may encourage it. While you are on drugs your partner can domi-
nate you. You may not argue with your partner because you haven't
got the confidence or self-esteem. Your subdued state may make life
easier for your partner, as he may be able to do just what he
wants.

Deciding to come of all your mood-altering drugs isn't an easy
step to take. It isn't simply a question of will-power as it is when you
stop eating cakes and chocolate. It's fighting an addiction—your
body and possibly your mind may be addicted to the drug. You are
fighting something that can control you, and that has been in control
of you for some time.

WHY WE DECIDED TO COME OFF

There are many reasons why people have stopped taking tranquillisers and sleeping pills. In a survey carried out at TRANX (UK)
we found the most common reasons were:

Unpleasant effects attributed to the drug	40%
Unable to stop taking them	21%
Want to do without them/taking them too long	16%
Ineffective	9%
Heard/told they were no good for you	6%
No reason given	3%

Ill on the pills

We may have become so ill that our illness may be controlling our
life. Because we may have lost our self-esteem and confidence, we
may find that we don't go out socially, friends aren't welcome to
visit, we can't go shopping without fear of a panic attack, we can't go
on public transport, we have stopped driving, we have given up
work—all in all, we have stopped 'living'.

Remember how Betty's 'post-natal' depression extended into her
son's years at school, and how she felt so ill every day she could only

lie on her sofa. She says: 'I was taking something because I felt dreadful but it made me feel worse. It was a vicious circle. What life did I have? What did I talk about? I was a cabbage.'

Changed character

'I met an old boyfriend who hadn't seen me in ten years,' says Liz. 'He was horrified at the shape I was in. Although he had known me on pills, I had had ten more years on them. He said, "You are so thin, what are you doing about it?" I replied I was under the hospital but they couldn't find anything wrong with me. He said, "Go and fight, go and do something." But my attitude was, what's the point? I had become subservient, trodden on and a defeatist. I'd given up on everything. He said to me, "You used to hold your head up, you used to be an attractive woman, and look at the state of you now. You are boring, you have nothing to say, you used to discuss things."'

As we discussed in Part Two, slowly, so very slowly, our character changes. It's hardly noticeable at first, as with many of the effects of tranquillisers and sleeping pills. It is only when we look back at the way we were before we took tranquillisers and/or sleeping pills that we realise we are no longer the same person. We might say to ourselves, 'I used to be happy-go-lucky. I used to laugh but now I'm miserable.' Or we might realise we've become more argumentative, snapping at the children at the slightest mishap. Remember that it was when I became violent that I began to suspect that the benzodiazepines were changing my personality.

I am an addict

Coming to terms with the fact that we are hooked on drugs can shock us into making the decision to come off. 'Dependent', 'addict' and 'hooked' have been words we've associated with alcoholics and heroin addicts, not someone who takes prescribed pills. But now in the harsh light of the truth we may realise there is little difference between those addicts and us; we need our 'fix' of tranquilliser, just like the junkie needs his fix of heroin or the alcoholic needs his whisky. We can't function without it. The only difference between the alcoholic and the hard drug addict and us is that those addictions are self-induced, whereas ours is iatrogenic—caused by the medical profession, and by our trust in it.

On drugs for too many years

We may have a 'gut' feeling that we shouldn't be taking these drugs. Deep down we know that taking drugs is wrong. Perhaps our original 'ailment' for which we were prescribed the drugs has long since passed. This is often the case when a mother is given tranquillisers for post-natal depression, and finds she is still on the drugs when her children have grown up and left home. I also fell into this category. I was prescribed drugs because my husband was violent towards me, yet I was still on the drugs and told I needed them when I had been divorced from him for over ten years.

The media

'I really didn't think there was anything wrong with tranquillisers until I saw a television programme about them,' says Suzanne. Television, newspapers and magazines have been full of the addictive nature of benzodiazepines. After all, the problem started to be recognised when Esther Rantzen did her first programme on TRANX (UK) in June 1983.

The day we decide to start our coming-off programme is the beginning of the end of our dependency.

II

COMING OFF

I came off my mood-altering drugs in December 1982. At that time very little was known about tranquilliser addiction and withdrawal. The vast majority of doctors still believed that benzodiazepines were harmless and non-addictive.

It happened when my own doctor, who had been prescribing me with tranquillisers and sleeping pills for seventeen years, retired. I had to find another practice. My new doctor was young and concerned. I casually asked him for my repeat prescription of pills: an assortment of benzodiazepines, barbiturates and antidepressants. He sympathetically enquired why I had been taking so many drugs for so long. I told him that my previous doctor had always said I needed them. He looked at me anxiously and said: 'I will not prescribe you any more pills. You don't need them at all. Go home, and that's the end of your pill-taking.'

Those words rang through my head. 'But I can't stop just like that.' I pleaded. 'I've been on them for seventeen years.'

'No more pills,' he insisted.

'But surely if I am to stop I should cut down slowly?'

'Go to work, that's your best medicine.'

'But doctor, I won't be able to go to work. I work with pills,' I stammered.

'Sorry, no more pills.'

I went home scared and worried about how I was going to cope. I
knew there wasn't a pill in the house—not in a jar or stashed away at
the back of a cupboard—because during the change-over of doctors I
had totally run out. I had nothing to help me.

The next morning, as I got out of bed, I felt giddy and sick. My
room swayed. I was incontinent. My whole body shook uncontrollably and my legs felt as though they were moving away underneath
me. I didn't wash or dress, but just sat in a chair in my nightie all day,
shaking. That evening a colleague from work, Hilary, came to see
me on her way home. To my surprise she said: 'You look marvel-
lous. I've never seen you look so well.' Shocked at her comment I
looked at myself in the bathroom mirror. It was true, I did look well.
My eyes were bright and shining, and I didn't look dopey any more.
But I felt as if I was going mad.

For days I wandered around my house without bothering to get
dressed or comb my hair. The shaking didn't cease, and more symptoms appeared. Now I had the feeling of an iron band around my head
and a bucket lying on my scalp. I couldn't co-ordinate, I couldn't
focus. My legs felt like jelly, and on the few occasions I got out of the
chair to walk, the ground was like waves. When my children spoke
to me I replied in slurred speech and back-to-front as if I was drunk.
But it was black thoughts that penetrated my soul—I could see no
way out of this gloom. I was desperate for help.

I went back to see my doctor. I crawled my way along the street,
steadying myself on fences and walls all the way to the surgery. As I
entered the consulting room I burst into tears. 'All I want to do is end
it all,' I sobbed. 'If it wasn't for my four children I'd throw myself
under a train.'

'That's your prerogative; if you want to jump, jump,' the
doctor replied coldly. 'But you are not going to get any more
pills.'

'Please, doctor, I need them. Look at me. I'm shaking like a leaf.'

'Go home.'

I was frightened. The pain, the shakes and the depression didn't
ease. I didn't know what was happening to me. But after a few days,
I had worked out a plan for getting my pills again. I found another
doctor whom I believed to be more lenient when it came to dishing
out the pills. I made the journey to the surgery like an old woman. In

the examination room, I cautiously asked for my long list of pills. The doctor nodded, picked up a pen and wrote out a prescription for every single one. Holding my prescription, I ran to the chemist. When the pharmacist handed me my bottles of pills, I sighed with relief. I unscrewed the top of the bottle of tranquillisers and asked the shop assistant for a glass of water. Within minutes of swallowing a pill I was feeling well again. I was 'normal'. I could carry on living. But mixed with this euphoria, I realised I couldn't survive without the pills. They were my life-line.

A few hours later, at home, I started to feel sick and I began to shake. I knew it was time for my pills again. Now I realised what was happening to me, but I wasn't going to give in this time. I wasn't going to have my life ruled by little pills. I went to the sink and emptied out the bottles of pills, one by one, except for the Valium. I turned on the tap and watched the water swirl the white, blue and yellow tablets around the sink until they slid down the drain. Then I sat down at the kitchen table with my bottle of Valium. I emptied out the contents and with a sharp knife cut each pill in half. Half I put back in the bottle, and half I threw away in the dustbin. From now on I was going to wean myself off.

Cutting the pills became a ritual. Every evening I would sit at my kitchen table measuring out the pills and cutting them into halves. When my hand was shaking too furiously, Judy, my teenage daughter, would cut them for me. I then placed the halves I needed for the following day into lids of bottles and lined them up on the windowsill. I had to do it this way because my mind was in such confusion that I often didn't know whether I had taken my pills or not. This way I couldn't go wrong.

As the halves became quarters I didn't trust my accuracy in cutting an equal amount, so Hilary helped. I would stand over her as she chopped the tiny half of the tablet into quarters, scrutinising the size with a magnifying glass, making sure I got the biggest quarter first. She wrapped up the unwanted pills in a paper bag and threw them away in the dustbin. But one day when she had left, I went to the bin to retrieve the pills. With newspapers spread across the kitchen floor I took out all the rubbish—the vegetable peelings, the tins and soggy teabags, until I found the paper bag holding my pills. As I picked it up, I dropped it like a hot plate on to the pile of rubbish. I rushed to the telephone and rang Hilary. 'You must come quick,' I said, 'I got the pills out of the bin, what am I going to do?' Within minutes Hilary was at my door. She cleared up the rubbish and took away the unwanted pills.

When I reached 2mg of Valium three times a day, I had a chance meeting with Dr David Marjot, Consultant Psychiatrist of St Bernard's Hospital Drug Dependency Unit in Ealing. He wanted to admit me into his wing. Hilary pleaded with me not to go into a psychiatric hospital. 'You'll be marked for life,' she said. 'It'll be on your files, don't go.'

'This doctor can help me,' I replied. 'I am too ill to face withdrawal on my own. What does it matter if people know I've been in that hospital if it is going to make me well?'

I was the first pure tranquilliser user to be admitted to the Drug Dependency Unit. The nurses sniggered at my addiction, they were used to dealing with alcoholics and heroin addicts. 'Who's ever heard of a tranquilliser addict,' they scoffed. But Dr Marjot warned: 'This woman is going to be very ill.' As he watched me suffer the harsh withdrawal symptoms he realised that people can become hooked on just a therapeutic dose of tranquillisers.

I continued to file down my pills in hospital, showing the nurses my method. By now I was down to 1mg, and my time between pills was lengthened as well. Every night they gave out the pills at the Drug Dispensary at 10 o'clock. To make sure I was always the first in the queue, I would start waiting at 8.30 p.m. But one night the nurse was late. It got to five past ten and she hadn't arrived, then ten past ten and still no sign of her. It wasn't until twenty past ten that the shutters to the dispensary were flung open. By then I was sweating, shaking and angry. The nurse handed me a speck of Valium. I stared at it: it was no bigger than a crumb. I had been waiting over two hours to swallow something that was the size of a pinhead. I thought, 'This is crazy—I've got to say farewell to Valium.' That was the last time ever I took a mood-altering drug.

Now that I was totally off, the withdrawal became more acute. 'I can't see properly,' I cried. Dr Marjot calmed me down and reassured me that my sight would return to normal, and it soon did. Wherever I sat I left a damp patch where I had been incontinent. It was embarrassing and humilating, especially as all the other patients were men. And every time it happened the nurses made me mop up my mess and wash my nightie.

The doctors' philosophy for my way to recovery was to keep me busy. Every day I would have to wash hundreds of dishes, but I dropped most of them as my hands were shaking furiously. 'It's all right if you smash the plates,' joked the nurse, when I told her it would be better if someone else did the washing up, 'we're insured.'

The physical pain hurt, but it was the emotional pain that was hardest to bear. Seventeen years of buried memories burst forth like a haemorrhage. Memories of my relatives and friends in Holland being sent to the gas chambers in the war, memories of my violent marriage, memories that I wasn't a good mother because of the drugs; memories that hadn't been dealt with all came flooding back. I cried, sobbed and whimpered day and night. It was during one of these black days that my daughter Judy came to visit me. She found me lying on my bed, my eyes sore and red, and tears rolling down my cheeks.

'Why are you crying, Mum? I've never seen you cry before. What's the matter?'

'I did so want to be a good mother to you all.'

'But you have been.'

She smiled down at me. Then the smile faded into a worried expression. 'When I got off the bus at the hospital, the bus conductor said this was a nut-house. Are you mad, Mummy?'

'No darling, I'm going to be well soon.'

As Judy turned to leave, I called her back. 'Oh, throw away any pills that are still at home!' She nodded.

My withdrawal lasted longer and was more severe than that of any of the alcoholics or hard drug addicts. After three weeks I was sent home for the weekend. There was going to be no warm welcome—I knew that, because my children were staying with friends while I was in hospital. But at least I would be in the comfort and warmth of my home.

It was a cold January day. Snow had fallen the night before. I trod up the path with the snow crunching underfoot and opened the front door. The house was flooded. Water was gushing out of a burst pipe on the landing. I walked through the icy water to the mains tap under the sink in the kitchen and I turned it off. In tears, I looked round at the water and the destruction it had caused. Then I caught sight of my bottles of tranquillisers lined up on the windowsill. Judy had forgotten to throw them away. I stared at the bottles of pills, and thought how much better I would feel, how easily I would be able to cope with this disaster if I took a pill. 'But no,' I said. 'I will not take one.' I picked up the bottles and threw them in the bin. Then I telephoned for the plumber and set to work cleaning up.

When I returned to the hospital the staff nurse looked at me. 'You've taken a pill,' she said accusingly. 'I can tell, you look awful.'

'No I haven't.' I pleaded. 'My house was flooded. I've been clearing up the mess all weekend.'

'A likely story,' she said. 'But there's only one way to find out if you're telling the truth, and that's with a urine test.'

'Why won't you believe me?' The humiliation welled up in me.

The next day the staff nurse apologised to me. There was not a trace of tranquillisers in my specimen. 'I wouldn't take another pill,' I said to her, 'and go through withdrawal again. Not for anything.'

After six weeks I was discharged from hospital. The nurses no longer scoffed at my withdrawal—instead they said: 'Valium is the driest of the dry Martinis.' They had learnt a lesson too. We all had learnt about withdrawal.

I was far from being well, but my GP was still unsympathetic and refused to give me a sickness certificate. So ten weeks into withdrawal I went back to work. As I was a one-parent family I had to look after my children too, as best as I could. But the withdrawal symptoms didn't ease. For months they carried on non-stop—as the shakes eased, the hot and cold flushes began; as those became less frequent I would feel giddy, and so it went on. The worst symptom for me stayed with me for many months, and that was the insomnia.

Then one night I slept. It was only then I could see I was going to get better and beat the addiction.

HOW TO COME OFF

The first stage of recovery

The reduction charts which follow are based on my experience with the thousands of clients I have successfully weaned off tranquillisers and sleeping pills. I was the first person to devise reduction charts for each of the benzodiazepines, and these charts are now used by doctors and others all over the world. In this book, I have given examples of how to wean yourself off Valium, Ativan and Normison.

Before you begin, discuss your withdrawal plan with your doctor.

Come off *slowly*. Don't stop 'cold turkey'.

Start today. Do not make excuses. Do not fear the emotional upheavals that *might* happen while you are cutting down. Life must go on. Of course, if you have just suffered a bereavement or are moving house it may be better to wait for a short time before you start your cutting-down programme, but do not wait for a 'perfect time', as that may never come. Make a decision and stay with it. Say to yourself, 'no matter how I'm going to feel, I am going to come off of my drugs.' Remember: you do not feel well *on* the drugs anyway.

When you have started your withdrawal plan, you shouldn't go back to taking a higher dose or other mood-altering drugs. It may only make withdrawal more difficult. Keep reducing slowly and consistently. Don't expect to get better quickly. You must give your body and your mind a chance to start healing very slowly. Remember how slowly you changed on the drug: now it takes time to get back to your normal self.

REDUCTION CHARTS

DIAZEPAM (VALIUM): LONG-ACTING ANXIOLYTIC

Obtainable in 10mg, 5mg, 2mg tablets and 2mg/5ml syrup.
Obtain 2mg tablets for your cutting-down programme.
Normal therapeutic dosage: 6mg–30mg (elderly 3mg–15mg) per day.

Reduce every 1–2 weeks

For example, your present dosage might be 20mg of Valium per day, taken as ten 2mg tablets.

	New daily dosage
Reduction 1	
Remove ¼ from *one* 2mg tablet	9¾ tablets = 19.5mg
Reduction 2	
Remove ½ from one 2mg tablet	9½ tablets = 19mg
Reduction 3	
Remove ¾ from one 2mg tablet	9¼ tablets = 18.5mg
Reduction 4	
Take 9 × 2mg tablets	9 tablets = 18mg
Reduction 5	
Remove ¼ from one 2mg tablet	8¾ tablets = 17.5mg
Reduction 6	
Remove ½ from one 2mg tablet	8½ tablets = 17mg

Please continue as above—syrup could be used for the final reduction.

N.B. If taking more than normal therapeutic dosage, first reduce by 5mg until you reach 20mg, when you can continue as above.

LORAZEPAM (ATIVAN): MEDIUM ACTING ANXIOLYTIC

Obtainable in 2.5mg and 1mg tablets.
Obtain 1mg tablets for your cutting-down programme.
Normal therapeutic dosage: 1mg–4mg (elderly 0.5mg–2mg) per day.

Reduce every 1–2 weeks

For example, your present dosage might be 4mg of Ativan per day, taken as four 1mg tablets.

	New daily dosage
Reduction 1	
Remove ¼ from one 1mg tablet	3¾ tablets = 3.75mg
Reduction 2	
Remove ½ from one 1mg tablet	3½ tablets = 3.5mg
Reduction 3	
Remove ¾ from one 1mg tablet	3¼ tablets = 3.25mg
Reduction 4	
Take 3 × 1mg tablets	3 tablets = 3mg
Reduction 5	
Remove ¼ from one 1mg tablet	2¾ tablets = 2.75mg

Reduction 6
    Remove ½ from one 1mg tablet   2½ tablets = 2.5mg
Please continue as above.

N.B. If taking more than normal therapeutic dosage, first reduce by a maximum of 1mg until you reach 4mg, when you can continue as above.

TEMAZEPAM (NORMISON): MEDIUM-ACTING HYPNOTIC

Obtainable in 10mg and 20mg tablets and 10mg/5ml syrup, in 10mg, 15mg, 20mg and 30mg Gelthix capsules, and as Normison in 10mg and 20mg capsules.

Obtain 10mg tablets for your cutting-down programme.

Normal therapeutic dosage: 10mg–30mg (elderly 10mg) per day.

Reduce every 1–2 weeks

For example, your present dosage might be 30mg (3 × 10mg) per night.

	New nightly dosage
Reduction 1	
Remove ¼ from one 10mg tablet	2¾ tablets = 27.5mg
Reduction 2	
Remove ½ from one 10mg tablet	2½ tablets = 25mg
Reduction 3	
Remove ¾ from one 10mg tablet	2¼ tablets = 22.5mg
Reduction 4	
Take 2 × 10mg tablets	2 tablets = 20mg
Reduction 5	
Remove ¼ from one 10mg tablet	1¾ tablets = 17.5mg
Reduction 6	
Remove ½ from one 10mg tablet	1½ tablets = 15mg
Reduction 7	
Remove ¾ from one 10mg tablet	1¼ tablets = 12.5mg
Reduction 8	
Take one 10mg tablet	1 tablet = 10mg

From now on slow down by changing to 5ml syrup – use Boots medicine tumbler to reduce intake millilitre by millilitre.

N.B. Your doctor may suggest the 'Planpack' reduction – in my opinion, this method is too fast.

If you change over from one drug to another you must first stabilise yourself on the new drug for a few weeks before reducing.

(As at March 1991)

The last milligram

That last quarter, that tiny little bit, may be the most missed if we don't take it. Dr Marjot suggests that is probably due to proportional reduction. 'If you come down from ten milligrams to nine milligrams, you've lost ten per cent. If you come down from one milligram to none, you've lost a hundred per cent. Different strengths of dosages and even liquid solutions (elixir) are available for most benzodiazepines for reduction purposes.

There is also that psychological pull of not wanting to give up the last bit. When that bit goes we have lost our 'crutch'. We have to face up to the fact that we are going to live our lives without drugs. Many doctors believe that to get over this hurdle of psychological dependence it is best to extend the cutting down process by means of a very small dose every other day.[42] But I have found that if we do this we throw ourselves in and out of withdrawal and we may feel worse on the days in between.

Is it possible to stay on a small dose?

No. As I said earlier on, to achieve full recovery we have to come off and stay off *all* mood-altering drugs. If we take one tranquilliser, sleeping pill or other sedating drug once a week or now and again, we are still dependent and will not be able to start full recovery. This dependence is often psychological: we have that comfortable feeling that the tranquillisers are there when we need them—just in case. Also, taking a small amount can increase the chance of craving to go back on to a higher dosage, because it keeps us continuously in a state of partial withdrawal, with the associated symptoms. And our recovery is held back.

Should I feel better before I reduce again?

Some doctors have the principle of waiting for one symptom to lessen before furthering the reduction programme. But I have found, by helping addicts at TRANX (UK), that the symptoms will not subside on a reduced dosage. I always advise my clients to carry on reducing even if the symptoms are severe.

Why you shouldn't come off 'cold turkey'

Abrupt withdrawal can be physically risky, in so far as it may lead to fits. But more to the point, slow withdrawal gives you and your brain time to adapt to living without a 'crutch'. It has been proved to be more successful.

When does withdrawal start?

Dr David Marjot has found that withdrawal symptoms may start within 21 to 24 hours, but they are frequently delayed and can occur as late as the second week of withdrawal or thereafter. This depends on the individual's metabolism and on the half-life of the drugs taken (see p. 196 for list of half-lives), particularly if a person has been on a high dosage for a long time. Symptoms can occur early on withdrawal of drugs with short half-lives, but may be delayed with longer-acting ones.

We may have already had some of the withdrawal symptoms while we were on the pills, but then we referred to them as side-effects (see p. 46). The full list of withdrawal symptoms can be found in Part Two.

The 'volcano' effect

As mentioned on page 21, while we've been taking benzodiazepines, they've been working on our brain, 'dampening down' the natural activity. Eventually our brain's own mechanisms for controlling anxiety and tension no longer function.

When we start to cut down our intake of the drug, our brain demands the full amount, but now we are not giving it what it wants. The brain is neither getting the drug it is used to, nor can it fall back on its own natural resources. So the nervous system goes haywire—it erupts. All our emotions and suppressed feelings come flooding out. Remember how I cried for everything that had happened in my life?

Our vulnerabilities come to a peak. And our adrenaline is charged. We are out of control, like a volcano exploding.

Sometimes when this happens we may feel that we are heading for a breakdown or going insane. We are not. Gradually, over the months of recovery, very slowly our brain will simmer down and should start sorting itself out.

HOW LONG DOES WITHDRAWAL LAST?

This question must be asked by every person coming off tranquillisers and sleeping pills. I cannot give an exact answer: the only thing I can say is that generally speaking withdrawal symptoms do not stop when you have taken your last pill. They can go on for many months, but I cannot put a time limit on them. All I can say is that the recovery process can be slow, so do not expect to get better fast. Of course there are also many people who experience few symptoms or even none at all, but they did not require the help of TRANX (UK).

The length of recovery depends very much on our own attitude towards it, and on how far we accept that all symptoms may be part of the recovery process and don't mean that we are suffering from a terminal illness or going mad. Also, our environment and the support of our family can influence our recovery.

At first I thought withdrawal was related to the length of time we had been taking the drugs. Some doctors believe that someone who has been on drugs for a short period of time will recover more quickly. I have found that this is not so. Someone who has been on for six months may take just as long to get better as someone who has been on for six or even sixteen years.

It has also been suggested by some doctors that the severity of withdrawal increases with the dose. Through my work at TRANX (UK) I did not find this to be the case. In fact, dose is relatively unimportant. Someone on a low dose can suffer withdrawal to the same extent as someone on a high dose. Dr Cosmo Hallstrom of Charing Cross Hospital and Profesor Lader proved this point in their research when they withdrew a series of patients who had been taking diazepam for an average of three years. A high–dose group (135mg daily) experienced reactions that were no worse than the reactions experienced by a low-dose group (20mg daily).

RECOVERY

Withdrawal is not like recovering from an illness or a disease. We may not see a slight improvement every day—it can be very erratic, with ups and downs. Dr Heather Ashton suggests that we do not lose the drug from our bodies at a consistent rate: it stays in our fat cells, brain cells and tissue cells, coming out in little spurts every now and then.[43]

The process of recovery can be different for everyone, but I have found that someone coming off tranquillisers usually falls into one of the following groups.

Waves   When you are cutting down your drugs you will most likely experience your withdrawal symptoms in waves. The 'waves' may carry on for some time, but each time the 'waves' should become less severe and the better periods in between usually become longer until the withdrawal symptoms diminish altogether.

Ill on the drugs   You may have been extremely ill on the drugs—you might even have been 'sectioned' or put in a psychiatric ward. When you are cutting down you may suffer from withdrawal symptoms, but once off you do not experience withdrawal symptoms at all.

IS IT WORTH IT?

Yes. But at some point during the recovery process, when we are off drugs completely, we may feel that we just cannot carry on. Some doctors may not realise that the symptoms we are experiencing are still withdrawal. This period may not be easy, but once over this hurdle we usually learn to accept any further relapses that may take place en route to recovery.

At first, we may only feel well for a few minutes a day. Hang on to these good periods, and try to remember them. They should keep coming back until eventually we are better. Even when we are over the worst of our withdrawal, we may still be vulnerable to anxieties for some time, while we are re-learning how to handle life on our own.

Remember: recovery may be tough, but the way through is to *accept* the symptoms for what they are (i.e. withdrawal), and to believe in yourself—*your* strength and *your* sanity.

SHOULD I CARRY ON WORKING WHEN I AM CUTTING DOWN AND IN WITHDRAWAL?

We may feel too ill to go to work—we may feel like crawling back into bed and hiding under the covers. But going to work can be one of the best therapies. Sitting at home feeling sorry for yourself will not get you better. Of course, it depends on the kind of work you do—it would not be advisable to return to a highly pressurised job. And I once told a dentist to take a long holiday! If you cannot work, keep busy with hobbies, gardening or housework. Remember that when I was in withdrawal, the nurses made me wash up the dishes even though I broke most of them. Do not be afraid of work and meeting people.

These ex-addicts worked and found that it helped them through withdrawal.

Vivian said, 'If somebody asked whether you should go back to work, I would say yes because I think after a while if you stay at home you have more time to dwell on the symptoms.'

Frank said, 'I only had a couple of weeks off work. I had to go in to work to support my family—that was the best thing I ever did. I could have sat at home and felt sorry for myself, but when I'm working I've got to get up at six o'clock. I've got to shave, look good, I've got to get out there and do it. I pulled myself together quicker than if I'd sat at home thinking I don't feel so well.'

Keith was annoyed that his wife made him go out to work. 'I thought how can she expect me to go through all this pain and go to work? She forced me to work and I thank God now that she did.

Nobody could praise her more than I do now, for making me carry on working.'

Keith, like most of the addicts, found work tough and terrifying. 'I used to cower down in the corner and be afraid of everybody and frightened that somebody was going to ask me to do something.' Keith realises now that if he hadn't gone to work his motivation would have been taken away, he would have become more depressed and finally he would have given in.

DOES MY AGE HAVE ANYTHING TO DO WITH LENGTH OF WITHDRAWAL?

I always feel that anyone over the age of 70 should give consideration to the possible long-term recovery time. However, many elderly people who have made the decision to come off have done so successfully.

Jean, who is 80 years old and is down to her last bit, said 'Today, I am very happy as I now see a light at the end of the tunnel. For years I was on pills, threatened with ECT and a stay in a psychiatric hospital—both I refused. I lost weight and most of my hair fell out. Now I have put the weight back on, my hair is growing and I treated myself to a soft perm, and I'm not a bit depressed when I look in he mirror—in fact, it cheers me up. But maybe, what is most rewarding is that I've been to the opera and I watched my grandson in his school orchestral concert. Not long ago I couldn't stand the noise of the electric kettle.'

Iris was another elderly woman who was determined to come off. She did so successfully when she was 80 years old. She admits that withdrawal and recovery were a battle, but she learnt to accept it. Now she is feeling well and leading a normal life. If she hadn't been guided by TRANX (UK) during her withdrawal, she knows that she would not have managed to wean herself off her mood-altering drugs. And instead of leading a busy life, she realises she could have ended up in a geriatric home. She thanked me, saying: 'There is one thing of which I am truly convinced: out of the ashes of what was once a happy, lively and active person, TRANX has recreated that happy being.'

CAN I TAKE ALCOHOL IN WITHDRAWAL?

No. Alcohol is a mood-altering drug. By taking alcohol instead of benzodiazepines we are only substituting one substance for another, so the pattern of dependency continues. The alcohol equivalent to tranquillisers is, for example:

2mg Valium *or* 0.25mg Ativan *or* 3.75mg Librium is equal to:

1 pub single of spirits
or
1 small sherry
or
1 glass of wine
or
½–⅓ pint of beer (depending on alcohol content)

It is best not to drink any alcohol until you have been free from all mood-altering drugs for at least a year, and always to remain aware that you have a dependent metabolism.

WOULD 'HERBAL' REMEDIES HELP WITHDRAWAL?

Relying on another pill, whether it is herbal or a tranquilliser, can create at least a psychological dependence. If we take a herbal remedy to sleep we may begin to depend on that instead of believing in our own capabilities. When we don't have that 'medicine' we might feel we cannot get to sleep without it. The only alternative to tranquillisers and sleeping pills is our inner strength and our own abilities.

HOW TO SURVIVE WITHDRAWAL

Do: Keep busy
Persevere
Go to a self-help group
Take exercises (swimming, walking, etc.)
Go gently through the day
Remember 'its the drug, not me'
Remember, you are the most important person in
recovery
Record the good moments you've had to look back on
See it through
Accept the withdrawal symptoms for what they are
Think of others worse off than yourself
Remember: we can get better

Don't: Get more tablets from your doctor than you need to
reduce
Take any other medicines to help you through (if it can
possibly be avoided)
Sit around doing nothing
Lie in bed during the day
Pressurise yourself
Rehearse and analyse symptoms to yourself
Expect it to be easy
Compare yourself with others
Drive (if it can be avoided)
Substitute alcohol for pills
Despair
Give up
Be frightened
Panic about panics
Feel guilty or ashamed
Expect others to understand

III

'DOCTOR—I WANT TO GET OFF'

Today, after the vast amount of publicity about benzodiazepines being addictive, most doctors in the United Kingdom appear to be more willing to wean their patients off the drug than before. But what is the doctor's attitude when we come off our pills? Is he sympathetic and encouraging, or not?

I have found that there are many differing opinions within the medical profession on the subject of withdrawal from benzodiazepines.

DOES YOUR DOCTOR BELIEVE WE ALL SUFFER FROM WITHDRAWAL SYMPTOMS?

Here people in the medical profession have widely conflicting views. At one extreme is Dr Peter Tyrer, who believes that only 30–45 per cent of tranquilliser addicts suffer withdrawal symptoms, whereas at the other extreme Professor Malcolm Lader states that 100 per cent of his patients reported withdrawal symptoms. [44] And I have only met very few ex-tranquilliser addicts who have come off without any adverse effects. Of course, those who withdraw from their drugs without a problem won't have had the need to go to a self-help group.

THE 'THEM AND US' SITUATION

How long withdrawal symptoms last is another widely disputed subject. Some doctors still believe recovery can be achieved within a couple of weeks, but Professor Malcolm Lader has reported: 'Symptoms have persisted for more than six months—in some cases for a year or more.'[45]

Emma's brother David was given false hopes of how quick his recovery would be when he was admitted into a private hospital to be weaned off his drugs. 'The psychiatrist told him: "in five weeks you'll be a different man and you'll come out laughing," ' says Emma. 'Well, five weeks later and five thousand pounds poorer, he came out, but he was not laughing. He was in a terrible state.'

Because the doctor is often unaware that withdrawal can last for many, many months instead of weeks, he may think his patient's original anxiety is coming back—withdrawal symptoms are, after all, anxiety symptoms. This, of course, may set the wheels in motion for the prescription of more drugs, with the explanation that the patient needs them and will most probably be on them for the rest of her life. By putting the patient back on drugs, the doctor makes her feel a total failure and she loses even more self-esteem. 'My doctor just told me there was something wrong with me and I needed tablets, which only made me feel insecure. I felt I was no one and not fit for anything,' says Sally.

If the patient is solely under the supervision of the doctor, she will in many cases most probably bow her head and believe that she can't live without drugs. She has little strength to argue—she is in the depths of withdrawal, and has little reason to believe that the doctor is wrong. After all he is the doctor—he should know. But if she is with a self-help group, like TRANX (UK), she is offered an alternative—a life without mood-altering drugs. This will put her into a situation of 'us and them'. The doctor says: 'go back on the drugs, you need them', and TRANX says: 'stay off, you should get better, believe in your inner strength.'

Sally had been off all her mood-altering drugs for a few months, but she was still very ill and suffering badly from withdrawal symptoms. She had an appointment with her psychiatrist and her husband took her along to his surgery. She had been under this psychiatrist most of her 25 years of pill-taking. Sally remembers sitting in his room with her husband beside her. The psychiatrist watched her trembling in the chair. 'Can't you see how ill you are,' he said, 'for everybody's sake—your husband's, your children's, please take at least antidepressants. It is not withdrawal you are suffering from.' Her husband was begging her to go back on the drugs too. Sally felt ill and vulnerable. The psychiatrist with all his knowledge was telling her to take drugs, and her husband whom she loved and didn't want to hurt was pleading with her too. But Sally had just joined TRANX, and we had told her: 'Don't go back on drugs.' She was torn between believing in TRANX and believing in her doctor—she didn't know who was right. But she knew that *she* desperately wanted to stay off these drugs. 'The guilt I would have felt if I had to go back on—all the good work coming off my tranquillisers and then to go on antidepressants—was too great,' she says. Sally did stay off her pills. She totally recovered and is now living a life free of pills.

The doctor may also be unaware that other 'drugs', such as alcohol, can spark off withdrawal symptoms again. Tim started drinking alcohol socially after a year of being off his drugs. 'I simply thought that my old trouble had come back again, the anxiety I used to suffer from. The way I saw it was, I'd been ill and the tablets had helped me. I thought I'd got better, and now I thought that for no reason my problems had come back. So I went to the doctor and said: "Look, I've got all this anxiety again that I used to have, what can I do?" And he said: "Well, the tablets helped you last time, go back on the tablets." I accepted what the doctor told me, that I was ill again, and had to take the tablets.' Tim stayed on the pills for seven years, but became more and more ill. Eventually after coming to TRANX he came off, but this time withdrawal was a lot harder. The second time around often is.

THE DOCTOR MAY BE TREATING HIMSELF

By prescribing drugs to his patients, the doctor may be treating himself. Just as he may have put his patient on tranquillisers because he couldn't cope with her problems and tears, so now he keeps her on drugs because *he* is worried about how *he* is going to cope with her withdrawal. He may not be trained to counsel her through recovery, and he may be apprehensive about whether his patient will really get better. Nor has he the time in surgery hours to be there for her when she needs to have his continuous reassurance that all the symptoms she is experiencing could be due to withdrawal. In a nutshell, to get his patient through recovery, the doctor has to say 'go home and feel ill', which goes against all his training. After all, he is a 'helping agent', and so he may see drugs as his only way out.

PART FOUR

BYSTANDERS

I

THE UNKNOWN SUFFERERS

'I've been robbed of my life, too.'
Husband of a tranquilliser addict

So far in this book we have dealt mainly with the effect tranquillisers have had on the user. However, there is another group of people who have never taken a benzodiazepine drug, but who may well have suffered because of them. Those people are the families and friends of the tranquilliser users.

When a pebble is thrown into the water, eventually the ripples hit the bank. In the same way the side-effects and withdrawal symptoms of tranquillisers cannot help but affect those people whom the addict loves. Although the spouse or the children do not experience the symptoms of the drug, they can go through their own version of hell, and be left with the scars. I call these people the 'unknown sufferers' because little attention has been given to them, and most doctors hardly realise their suffering exists. Even specialists who have devoted their work to the effects of tranquillisers appear to have virtually ignored the effect the drug has had on the family of the addicts. Also, and maybe more to the point, the addict may not always realise that her loved ones are going through their own pain. She may be so wrapped up in herself that she cannot see beyond her own symptoms.

THE PARTNER

There are three different types of partners of a tranquilliser addict.

1. The innocent bystander who watches helplessly as wife or husband falls into the tranquilliser trap, wanting to help but not knowing how to.

2. The person who has an unstable relationship with his or her partner which has resulted in the wife or husband taking tranquillisers. When the addict is off mood-altering drugs the problems of the marriage need to be faced.

3. The person who *wants* to be in control—to do everything for the addict and make all the decisions. They *want* their partners to be dependent on them. And they may be the reason why the drugs are taken. A husband may say: 'My wife cannot come off these drugs—I have to do everything for her.' Here the husband is playing 'power games'. Often when the tranquilliser addict has come off the drugs and starts becoming more self-assertive the relationship may end in divorce, because the ex-addict will not accept being told what to do any more.

COPING WITH 'THEIR' SYMPTOMS

The addict has the symptoms, but you, as the spouse or child (the unknown sufferer), experience the knock-on effects. You have to bear the brunt of their pain, numbness, anxiety, depression, phobia or insomnia. You are the one whom the addict hits out at or clings on to. So what are the problems of being in that firing line?

NOT BEING LOVED

Let's take numbness of feeling. We've heard how the addict may not feel any more—her emotions may be dead. She may not care, love or cherish; she may not laugh or cry; she may not have the desire to make love. Her feelings are in a vacuum.

Loving someone but not being loved, caring for someone but not being cared for, can be painful and wounding. Obviously it may cause a lot of friction within the relationship, and can demand a lot from the spouse. As one husband says, 'My marriage revolves around my wife absolutely, her symptoms. It's always me saying, "How are you?" She never asks how I am. I feel deprived of understanding, sex, you name it.' The addict wants to be loved and wants to be cuddled, but she may not be able to love and cuddle in return. She may be unable to give, she may only take. She is like a newborn baby who needs love but cannot give love. Gloria saw it as a cry for help. She says: 'I was saying help me, love me and try to understand what I'm going through. Try and understand how bad this is for me.'

Along with the lack of showing love there is the lack of making love, which obviously causes an enormous sense of rejection for the spouse. As Jenny says, 'The time when the sexual feelings went, that was the time when we had more rows because he would reject me completely. I would make the approach, get him in the mood—and nothing. That's really hard to cope with. If the sexual side of the relationship isn't right, then it affects how you operate as a couple. That horrible feeling of rejection is awful and I had done nothing wrong. There I was trying to help and he just rejected me.'

The natural mother's or father's love for a child may be lost too. When my daughter Judy was twelve years old she felt I didn't love her because I couldn't show my feelings. The pain became so intense for her that she wrote me this note: 'To love, you must be loved. To enjoy life, you must be enjoyed.'

In Part Two, Vivian describes how she would say to her daughter Katie, 'I love you,' but she didn't know what the feelings of real love were any more. She would say the words but they meant nothing to her. Vivian tried to cover up this lack of feeling for her daughter by saying what she ought to say. But even a child of six years old could see through the pretence. Katie felt that the words spoken by her mother were shallow because Vivian didn't demonstrate her love by playing with her. 'All Mummy used to do,' says Katie, 'was lie in bed. I didn't really like it because I had no fun with her or anything. Or when I was reading a book she could never listen to it. She just didn't care because she was so sick. It wasn't very nice at all because I always used to have to do everything by myself, but now (she's off) I do things with my Mummy.'

Numbness of feeling can also make the addict look as if she is cold and without a conscience, which, of course, she most likely is—but it's the drug that has done this to her. The spouse or child at the receiving end of this unfeeling attitude will undoubtedly be affected and may be hurt. When my youngest daughter left home at sixteen to live with a friend's family, I didn't show any remorse because I couldn't—my feelings had been wiped away by the drugs. Of course, my daughter interpreted my behaviour as unloving and uncaring. She believed that I was glad she had left. After all, how could she have thought otherwise?

The cause of the lack of emotions is often only discovered by the spouse and children when the addict is off all mood-altering drugs and the natural feelings are able to start surfacing again. Then the family can look back in retrospect, as my daughter Maira did. 'From the time my Mum took these tablets her life really was at a standstill. She could not go forward and she could not go back. She was there as a person but there were no emotions. She functioned. She went through the day by the clock and with a rigid routine—we knew what was going to happen every minute of the day. But when she started coming off, she started laughing. The first time she laughed, it hit me—I had never heard my Mum laugh before! It was also the first time I saw her cry or show any emotions. It was a shock, I sort of stood back and thought "Oh!" I had suddenly realised I had not seen my mother do this before. It felt wonderful that there was something behind that mask.'

Lack of motivation—its effect

When the tranquilliser user doesn't want to go out, meet people, have friends to visit or go on holiday, it obviously can have a great impact on the spouse and children's lives.

John and June's marriage totally changed during June's thirty years of pill-taking. He was a financier, which involved wining and dining clients. At the beginning of June's addiction she would force herself to go out to business dinners with her husband, but she found it a great strain. 'You are supposed to be like a companion,' she says, 'but socially if you sit there and say virtually nothing at the dinner table, you are a disaster. People dread having to take you out. That's what used to happen because I was so busy worrying about my pills, my breathing, my stomach, my this and that, I wasn't a very social person. If I could avoid going out with him, I did.' Eventually, John had to attend business dinners and social occasions by himself.

Holidays also became an ordeal not only for June, but for John too. As June took extra pills for the flight, she ended up suffering from withdrawal when she arrived at her holiday destination: because of the increased dose, her body was craving for more. 'I was in bed for a lot of the time on every holiday we went on,' she confesses. 'The holidays were wrecked totally. Financially it wasn't nice to spend a lot of money only to find when you got to the holiday resort that you were in bed. In the end my husband rather expected me to be in bed when I got there.' Eventually June became totally housebound, and so did John. He recalls, 'For about eight years we never moved out of the flat. No holidays or anything like that.'

Children miss out. It starts at a very young age when the mother may not even take her child to the playground in the park. Katie was seven years old before Vivian took her to the park, and that was only when Vivian was off all mood-altering drugs. Vivian had tried desperately hard to be the mother she should have been to Katie. She felt extremely upset that Katie was missing out on outings because of the 'illness' which she later discovered was an addiction. So for Katie's sixth birthday, Vivian decided to hold a party. She invited thirty children.

Vivian had just come off her tranquillisers a few days before. She had been suffering from panic attacks, agoraphobia, tiredness and palpitations, but on the day of the party she could not lift her arm out of the bed. She took an extra 1.5mg of benzodiazepine to see her through the day. Her body didn't know what had hit it—she had a racing heart, dizziness and an unbearable feeling of unreality. Vivian survived the party but collapsed the moment the last guest had left. She then stayed off her drugs. By the time her daughter's seventh birthday came round, she invited thirty children again. This time, Katie and her mother enjoyed themselves.

Later on in teenage life, the child's social life may be affected. My daughter Maira remembers: 'We were never allowed to invite friends over, so we were hardly ever invited back to their house. We did realise that other families were different, in the sense that other teenagers were allowed to play their music loud in their bedrooms and have several friends over, but their mothers never told them to be quiet.' I didn't allow my children to play their music or have friends over because I was oversensitive to noise (see page 78).

Another teenage son, Roy, was embarrassed when he couldn't invite his friends into his home because his mother found it such a strain. 'My friends would turn up on the doorstep, so I couldn't say "go away". I'd let them in and then Mum's act would come on: 'Oh, I'm fine,' she'd say. And she'd sit down and chat to them. When they went she looked absolutely knackered. But I couldn't say to my friends "you can't come round" and explain why, because I didn't know the reason myself, and at the same time I didn't want to have them round and make Mum feel bad.'

Likewise, his mother put up a front for her son's friends because she was guilty and embarrassed about the reasons why he couldn't invite his friends into their home. 'If I could say to Roy, "I can't iron your shirts; I've two broken arms", that would make sense because he'd understand. How do you say to your son, "You can't have your friends over because that makes me uneasy, scared, I can't put up with it." It's very difficult for me to own up that I can't cope with something I feel I should be coping with.'

Living with someone else's phobia

If the addict becomes agoraphobic, so the unknown sufferers, the spouse and children, may also lead a more home-centred life, as John's account has already shown. Agoraphobia can also create role reversal within the family: this is discussed later on in this chapter.

The unknown sufferer can be prey to other obsessions too. When Karen had a cleaning obsession which meant that she couldn't stop dusting, washing and polishing from morning until night, it affected her husband, Mark, when he decorated the house. He explains, 'It wasn't uncommon for me to work a full week decorating from seven-thirty in the morning until eleven at night in a mad attempt to finish because Karen would get so agitated if things were not done. I

made all sorts of compromises to make everything go along hunky
dory, but it was taking drugs which was the compromise.'

Even the children notice their parents' phobias, if only to mock
them, as Keith's children did with the hypochondria that developed
on the drugs. 'It got to the pitch,' says his wife, 'where even the
children noticed. If any disease or anything was mentioned the children would nudge each other and say: "Dad will have that next
week".'

The arguments

'You are not talking about an argument that stops. Because of the
tranquillisers the argument doesn't stop, it would just go into hys-
teria to the point where I was quite terrified. There was no end to the
arguments. It wasn't a case of me walking out and saying "I'll go
down to the pub", which is what most couples might do if there's an
argument. I'd never get across the street, I mean the way would
physically be barred. Physical contact would always happen, so
without it becoming violent there was nothing I could do to escape,'
says Mark.

Mark talks about arguments that do not stop but go on and on.
When the tranquilliser addict starts to argue she cannot put the brake
on, she cannot think 'If I carry on any more, the argument will only
get worse.' She has no control over her actions any more. Mark
could control himself by not becoming violent, but his wife
couldn't: she physically barred his way. The argument may be
minor and totally illogical, but it can get out of proportion. It's as if
the argument consumes the addict.

Living with someone else's depression

Not knowing how to cope with the addict's bleak outlook on life can
cause the spouse to become depressed. A husband reveals how he
feels: 'Seeing someone who is constantly depressed, constantly
frightened, who never seems to be in touch with reality, as I am
myself, makes one feel almost alone. One has a partner who, to all
intents and purposes, isn't really there. It is actually depressing being
with someone you feel just isn't there. My wife often says, "I don't

think life is worthwhile." I don't say it, but it isn't worthwhile for me either. I'm a happy person, I've retired. I just want the simple pleasures in life, but in a way I'm barred from those because this is a twenty-four hour thing.'

This husband also finds the ups and downs of depression hard to understand and cope with. 'I would go out with my wife in the car, have a nice ride in the countryside. We'd laugh, look around the country market stalls, maybe we'd buy something. Then suddenly without any reason whatsoever, there's a complete change into depression. "I know I'm going to die," she says. That actually frightens me. It startles me and I'm not easily startled. The unpredictability of the whole thing actually frightens me. Or we can have a good day, go to bed at night and she's quiet and contented. Then about three o'clock in the morning she starts crying, "I know I'm going to die." That's what gets me.'

Children of an addict aren't spared the pain either when it comes to depression, no matter how hard the parents try to protect them. Wendy, a mother and an unknown sufferer, explains what effect her husband's depression had on their children. 'My eldest daughter was going to leave home. She was only thirteen years old. She was crying all the time because her Dad was crying all the time. She couldn't stand it because her Dad was meant to be the boss. All of a sudden he wasn't anything. She couldn't handle that. You see, at thirteen it was her time when she starts being a woman—so she had her own problems. But I wasn't there to deal with them because I was dealing with him. I tried not to shut her out but it was very difficult. When my other children came home from school and saw Harry crying his eyes out, or they couldn't go out or have anything—it hurt them. It affected our eighteen-month-old baby as well. Now he won't sleep in his bed, he sleeps in our bed. He won't let me out of his sight.'

Another 'baby' to look after

Descriptions such as 'just like a baby' or 'another child' are often used by the unknown sufferer when they talk about their addicted partner. The addict may have totally lost her self-esteem and confidence and be incapable of making decisions. Sometimes it can reach the stage where she is frightened to be alone. The addict may become emotionally dependent on the unknown sufferer. But does the spouse (unknown sufferer) want to take on this added responsibility? Can the spouse cope? Three wives talk about what it was like having an addict for a husband.

Wendy, Harry's wife said: 'Looking after him was just like looking after a baby. I couldn't draw back the curtains. I couldn't let him see the postman. If I drew back the curtains or let him see the postman, he'd do his nut. So we'd have to live with the curtains shut for a while because he couldn't take that. He'd suffer from terrible nightmares. I wasn't allowed to go to sleep until he went to sleep. He was terrified someone was going to get him. We'd sit up in bed, my eyes being held open by matchsticks. He'd say "don't go to sleep, don't go to sleep" until he'd drop off, then I'd be allowed to. I couldn't even go to the toilet on my own. He had to come with me. That went on for a long time—about a year.'

Ann, Keith's wife, found that as she had to take on more responsibilities, her role changed. 'Over a period of time my husband didn't want to be bothered with any responsibilities, whereas before he used to take care of everything. He used to always see to the money and holidays and things like that. I just sort of took it over. I was in charge because he wasn't really capable of making a decision. A lot of the time it was a case of leading him around by the hand. I'd have to go and sit with him in his business because he just couldn't cope on his own. As long as I was there it was fine, he could cope. During the day he'd phone me from work and tell me how ill he felt, and I used to think "God, I can't cope with this."'

Another wife found it frustrating and emotionally draining having to make all the decisions, right down to what her husband was going to wear. 'I had to do everything for him. The only thing I didn't do was take him to the toilet. He'd ask "What shirt shall I wear?"; "Have I got my vest and pants?"; "Where are you going?"'

Just as much emotional strain is put upon the husband when he is the unknown sufferer. He may be torn between having to work to pay the mortgage and bills and looking after his wife.

Peter, Nickie's husband, said: 'She was phoning me at work all the time, almost constantly. I got into a hell of a lot of trouble over it. She couldn't cope with the cooking and shopping. I used to have to do it. In the end I had to give up work. She couldn't cope with the children and the normal things in the home. Obviously I wanted to work—we needed the money. But when you are forced into that situation you have to make that choice, and we did go on for a long, long time trying to cope, trying to look after the children, trying to cope with the home. I was trying to cope with going to work and helping and all that.'

Another retired husband talks of living with his addicted wife. 'I daren't not be there. She wouldn't go anywhere at all without me. There's no relaxation. It's awful for her, she's the one who is suffering, but the partner suffers too, if he really cares. There's no real sharing. My wife would love to but it's the lack of motivation.'

Anxiety creating anxiety

Anxiety in the addict may cause the spouse (the unknown sufferer) to become anxious. The constant worry of looking after a tranquilliser user, the helplessness in watching a happy person turn into someone who may be in the depths of depression and the torments of withdrawal can all contribute to the spouse suffering from anxiety as well.

John was anxious about his wife June when she went out, as a father might be concerned over a young child. 'I was terrified when she went out on her own, wondering what would happen to her. She'd leave her credit card behind in the shop, she'd sign blank forms. Once when she had a panic attack in a store, a fellow saw she was in great distress and offered her a lift in his car. He brought her home. It was very nice of him but it was a very dangerous thing for her to have done.'

Betty's husband became more and more anxious because he couldn't stand the pain of watching his wife suffer for so long. 'He couldn't handle the situation at all,' Betty says. 'He nearly went to pieces through it all. He was absolutely petrified to watch me being so ill. He didn't know whether I'd ever get well because I hadn't been well for eighteen years. At one time he got himself in such a state, the doctor almost gave him an antidepressant to help me.'

Ann also suffered. She had a breakdown over her husband's addiction. 'In the end, I couldn't take any more. It used to destroy me when he'd come home. He'd start to eat his dinner then he'd push it away and just sit there and cry. One night, I nearly did walk out on him. But my son came home and I just burst into tears.' Ann needed a shoulder to cry on. She couldn't cope with her husband's troubles as well as her own. She had given him everything she had to give. When he came off tranquillisers and began to recover she felt as if 'a weight had been lifted from my shoulders'. She no longer had the responsibility of looking after him, nor did she have to cope with his symptoms.

Even children of an addicted parent may be affected by the fears of anxiety. Vivian remembers what happened to her daughter when she suffered a panic attack. 'Once I took Katie to see a film. The show started and I had a massive panic attack. Katie suddenly said, "Mummy let's go home. I'm not well. Please take me home." I tried to make out everything was fine. When my panic attack subsided I said to her, "Do you want to go home?" "No," she replied "I think I'm fine now."' Katie was scared about how she was going to look after her mother.

WHAT DO I DO?

You may feel very much alone when you are the unknown sufferer—the spouse, partner or child of a tranquilliser addict. Just as the addict is trapped, not knowing how to get out of the tranquilliser maze, so the unknown sufferer can be trapped, not knowing how to help, comfort and carry on living a normal life. There may be the great sense of helplessness that John felt during his wife's withdrawal. 'Unfortunately the pains of withdrawal can't be shared. The addict has to carry those all herself. The family may watch in sympathy, but they are quite helpless. I couldn't do anything. I could only give moral support. Try to understand the problems—yes. Share the problems—yes. But in terms of doing something physical or something practical, I didn't know what to do. Does anybody? I think it's a complete helplessness from the family's point of view. All they can give is understanding and patience.'

Not knowing what to do or how to help the addict may create a feeling of guilt in the unknown sufferer. Roy, Doris's eighteen-year-old son, wanted to help his mother, but he didn't know how. It reached a peak when his mother's suffering came into conflict with his own social life. 'I was getting ready to go down to the pub,' he says. 'I went downstairs, and Mum was sitting there really upset. That didn't make me feel particularly wonderful. So I wanted to stay and chat because I wanted to help, but at the same time Mum knew I wanted to go out, so she was feeling bad because I wasn't going where I wanted to go. So I'm in an awkward situation, because I wanted to stay and help but at the same time by staying I'm making her feel guilty because I'm not with my friends. So we both were feeling guilty about each other—no one is winning. So what do I do? Do I go and leave her upset, or do I stay and make her feel guilty? I didn't know what to do for the best. I wanted to help her, yet by helping her I was making it worse.'

If sympathy doesn't seem to make the tranquilliser addict feel better, then the unknown sufferer may resort to other methods. One way is to use the 'buck-yourself-up' attitude. Frank's wife Jenny said, 'It had gone on for so long, it got to the stage when I would try the tactic of "come-on-pull-yourself-together".' But of course, Frank was totally unable to shrug off the depression because he was under the influence of the drugs, and so out of control.

Because both the addict and the unknown sufferer can be in this tranquilliser 'web', they may not be able to see the way out. They may go to the doctor seeking help, but are more often than not sent home with more or other drugs. 'The worst thing for me,' says Jenny, 'was that I let it go on and on purely because I didn't know how to get out of it.'

Allowing the addiction to go on for such a long time, and even wishing the addict would take a pill, may create feelings of guilt in the unknown sufferer. 'I still wonder,' says Karen's husband, 'why did I allow Karen to take those tablets for such a long time? I'm as responsible as anyone, I've allowed it to go on. At the time it was an easier route to take because when Karen was getting het-up and anxious I said, "take a tablet".' So many unknown sufferers have taken the same road—running away from the situation by telling the addict to take another pill—only because they are frightened, ignorant and don't know how to help.

YOU CAN'T SEE THE PAIN

Although the unknown sufferer may take the brunt of withdrawal, he mustn't let the addict see the knocks and bruises. There may be no one trying to smooth down the rough ride of withdrawal for the unknown sufferer. No one is there to help and no one understands. Wendy explains how she coped during her husband's withdrawal: 'It was a nightmare. Even though he went through it, I think I went through it worse than he did. There was no one to talk to me. I would have to deal with him, then I had to sit in the toilet and cry my eyes out and come out as happy as a sandboy to keep him topped up. If I felt down, I couldn't tell him. I didn't have anyone to talk to the whole time he was ill. I had to cheer him up and I'm thinking "Why can't someone cheer me up?" No one could because I had no one to talk to. No one even said "Do you want a rest or do you want to go out?" No one would do it. Mind, he wouldn't have stayed with anyone.'

To protect the addict the unknown sufferers 'have to learn to be very good actors. They have got to put on brave faces, they can't let the addict know that they are suffering,' explains a partner. Some turn to religion. 'When I am cutting the pills in halves and quarters, I'm praying. Sometimes I get emotional inside, but I can't show her that side of my feelings. I sit and cry on my own. I've prayed a lot.'

The only way the unknown sufferer can receive understanding and help is through self-help groups, which are discussed in Part Six.

TAKING ON ANOTHER ROLE

When one of the partners in a relationship is an addict, the other partner may take over their role, whether it be mother, father, wife or provider, simply because the addict is likely to lose confidence, self-esteem and the ability to make decisions. Ann, whose story is told on page 130, is a typical example of how the wife can take on the role of dealing with the family's finances because her husband Keith could no longer make decisions. She became the more dominant partner and the one who 'wore the trousers'.

Often husbands are found to take on the role of shopping and dealing with household duties because the wife feels she cannot do these tasks any more. Either she just hasn't got the physical ability, or she can't cope because she can't make decisions. 'Bill does the shopping,' says Doris. 'I get into the most incredible state making out the shopping list because one of the things that's happened to me is not being able to make decisons.'

Even young children have to take on more responsibility at a very young age, as did Vivian's daughter Katie. 'I just had to look after Mummy. When she had a headache, I'd give her something to go on her head to make it go away.'

HIDING THE ADDICTION

'My wife's addiction is a dark family secret. My son doesn't even know.'

This is a typical trait of a tranquilliser addict. If the addict is a parent they often want to hide their addiction or how ill they feel from their children. They believe they are shielding them from the misery of the dependence. But the children may end up feeling guilty when their parent's addiction comes to light, thinking that if they had known about the dependence, they could have supported or co-operated more.

Roy experienced this. His mother for many years had hidden from him how ill she had felt. Whenever he rang home from college she would tell him she was feeling well, even if she felt very depressed. As with most teenagers, he would ask her to do certain things and she would oblige even though she felt ill. Eventually Roy learned about his mother's dependence. 'It made me feel pretty guilty,' he says, 'because I didn't know about it. If I'd known anything about it I could have helped in some way or other. I feel angry to a certain extent—cheated. I wish she'd shared it with me a bit more. Just by my being at home she was under pressure. Maybe I could have lessened that if I'd known something about it or known just how bad she was. If I'd known what was going on, I could have explained it to my friends. I wouldn't have thought: why doesn't she want them around here or why does she feel so ill when they come round?'

SOCIALISING

As we have mentioned, the social life of the unknown sufferer may be affected. John's life became home-centred when his wife became agoraphobic. Children may miss out on having their friends over or having parties.

If the addiction started during the marriage and the partner has witnessed a change in the tranquilliser user, then the partner may be able to accept the change. But if the addiction started before the marriage, the partner (unknown sufferer) may believe the marriage is at fault. Bill married Doris when she had been taking drugs for some years. It was a second marriage for both of them. 'I knew Doris was taking pills but it didn't mean anything to me—most people take pills for a condition, it was just accepted that's what she was doing. But once we were married, then things like the apprehension of meeting people became more pronounced. The first year we were married there was a Christmas ball at work. I just expected Doris would be able to come to it without any problem whatsoever and then of course when it came to the time, I realised how much of a problem it was to her.

'It made me nervous for her because if she was going to be so worked up and concerned about going to these things, then I didn't particularly want her to feel that way. In fact, there were one or two things that we were invited to through the firm that I never even told Doris about because I thought if I told her she would be determined to go for my sake, because she didn't want to let me down. After going to the few functions it was enough to show me that it was physically and mentally getting to her, to go to things that to me were just part of life. Initially I did wonder why she was doing this to me and my friends. Is it me, something I am doing that I shouldn't be doing, or have I upset her, or is she sort of anti-me or my friends? And when we kept on refusing invitations, I could see my friends were thinking that this must be a funny excuse, she can't be ill for this length of time, or that they maybe don't want to come. Or maybe Doris doesn't want to come and she is stopping me from going.'

Friends can be inclined to turn their back on a tranquilliser addict, as Wendy and Harry found out. 'There's not one person who wants to know you because you are an outcast. As far as friends are concerned, they avoid us completely. We are like the plague.' So it is not only the addict who loses friends, but the unknown sufferer too.

Because children may not be able to bring a social life into the home of an addicted parent, they may seek it out of the home. Often the addicted parent is unaware of what is happening. Maira, my daughter, saw my addiction as her freedom. 'I made the most of my teenagehood, which others could not have done. I didn't keep to the restrictions because I knew my Mum would have taken her pills to sleep. I had my freedom from the age of thirteen without her realising it.'

WORK

For the partner, work is often looked upon as a sanctuary away from dealing with the torment of the tranquilliser addict—a place where he can be himself, where he can get on and lead a normal life. But often this sanctuary is threatened when the addict telephones or tries to stop her partner from going to work. Also the partner has the financial worries of keeping home and family afloat. When Margaret started to plead with her husband to stay at home, he replied, 'I've got to pay the mortgage, we've got to carry on living, we've got to carry on as normally as possible, and the only way we can do that is by me keeping going.'

The partner's work may be affected, and so much so that it can prevent promotion or expansion of the business. 'My husband wanted to do lots of things,' says Betty, 'expand his business, but he always felt that he couldn't because he had a sick wife. He had the responsibility of me and the kids, and he didn't feel he could get on and do what he wanted in life because I was such a sick person. He said he never knew how he was going to find me when he walked through the door.'

FINANCIAL HARDSHIP

It is inevitable that the family will fall on hard times when the breadwinner is an addict. The addict may not be able to carry out the tasks his job requires because of the side-effects and withdrawal symptoms he is experiencing. An employee may find that he is fired; an employer may find his business collapsing, as Harry did.

Harry had a successful ladies' fashion business. He had his own factory and a number of boutiques. He was prescribed tranquillisers when he moved house and suffered from anxiety and depression. 'As soon as I became addicted to tranquillisers, that's when my business went downhill. It took me eight years to build up from a basement to a medium-size factory supplying top stores. And it took just two years for it to grind to a halt. I didn't know what was wrong, I didn't even suspect anything, least of all the pills. I just thought I was tired. I thought maybe I should get out of the business and have a long rest. Daily I was losing my confidence. It was dropping, which doesn't help because in the fashion business you have to be on the ball. You can't sit back. Also I was getting more and more depressed. The depression built up every day. In the end I couldn't be bothered to do anything. Then I couldn't pay the bills. We had to re-mortgage our house. We were living on social security. It ruined us.'

CAN THE MARRIAGE SURVIVE?

There is no doubt that the marriage can be put under a tremendous strain when one of the partners is a tranquilliser addict. So many marriages end up in divorce. Time and time again partners have said to me, as Ann did, 'If we hadn't had a strong marriage, I could have quite easily got up and just walked out.'

Of course, it is difficult for a marriage to survive when one of the partners has changed character. And it is especially pronounced when a confident person becomes dependent and subordinate on drugs. Very often the marriage breaks up when the addict is off mood-altering drugs and her new self-assertive character has developed. The partner may not like this new confident person: he may have preferred it when he was in control.

THE UNBORN CHILD

There is now a growing worry that benzodiazepines taken during pregnancy can affect the baby. 'The drugs readily enter the foetus,' says Dr Heather Ashton, 'and can depress vital functions in the newborn infant.' The concentrations of the drugs are higher in the baby than in the mother because the baby can't metabolise them. Once the drugs have got into the baby, the baby can't get rid of them.[46]

In its first few days the newborn baby may suffer from the 'flopping infant syndrome', with respiration difficulties, hypothermia and failure to start sucking. Then, about two or three weeks after the birth, the baby may become hyperactive or appear to be suffering from colic. Now the baby may be going through the withdrawal symptoms, such as tremor, irritability, hyperactivity, breathing problems and vigorous sucking.[47]

A Swedish report studied eight children born to mothers who had taken benzodiazepines during their pregnancy, and found that they had 'facial and severe central nervous system abnormalities'. Many of the abnormalities were similar to those of babies born to mothers who are alcoholics. The report stated among many findings that the children did suffer from withdrawal symptoms and had a low birth weight. They also found that there was a lack of rooting and sucking reflexes, and that most had feeding difficulties. Facial malformations were mainly around the eyes and nose (such as cleft lip). Six of the babies had various degrees of mental retardation.[48] However, Dr Heather Ashton points out that in general the risk of these abnormalities happening is very low.

Benzodiazepines also enter the breast milk, so the nursing mother could be sedating the infant.

If you are already pregnant and still taking benzodiazepines, Dr Bhatt points out the pros and cons of withdrawing from the drug in that condition:

Severe withdrawal symptoms may cause a miscarriage.

If you are on a high dosage, try to come down slowly to a therapeutic level. Then finish withdrawing after the baby is born.

If you are on a small dosage, slowly withdraw and come off, provided there are no severe symptoms.

If the choice is between coming off the drugs and going through withdrawal or staying on the drug with the possible side-effects, severe withdrawal may have a worse effect on the baby. If you are considering getting pregnant and you wish to come off your tranquillisers, it may be advisable to come off before getting pregnant.

HOW THE UNKNOWN SUFFERER CAN HELP AN ADDICT

Through my work at TRANX I have found that the family can fall into one of three categories: the over-indulging family, the under-indulging family and the supportive family.

The over-indulging family This family may be affected by the addict suffering from the 'poor-little-old-me' syndrome. Of course, the addict is ill. She feels she cannot cope with the shopping, household tasks, travelling, socialising—but that doesn't mean she has to give up on life completely. If the family is always doing the shopping, cooking and all the other day-to-day tasks for her, it doesn't give her the opportunity to learn to cope again. She is unlikely to get better by just sitting in a chair or staying in bed. She will only recover by starting to face life, little by little. In other words, she has to learn to 'walk' again, without drugs.

The under-indulging family This family simply do not want to know about the addict and her symptoms. They may have the 'pull-yourself-together' approach. And they may be quick to encourage her to take another tablet to keep her quiet—it suits them.

The supportive family This family may never fully understand the feelings of the addict, but they are morally supportive and give continued encouragement, reminding her that better days should be ahead if she perseveres. Their concern and strength is of great value if her determination weakens. They have to be *very* patient and may often have to listen to her temporary obsession with 'the problem'. They may even have to foot enormous phone bills, because much support is needed from others who have overcome their dependence.

HANDY HINTS FOR HELPFUL HUSBANDS (AND WIVES)

The list below was devised by John when he was helping his wife recover from her tranquilliser addiction.

1. Don't show annoyance. (She can't help moaning!)

2. Do help her plan a timetable for the reductions.

3. Do show an interest in the withdrawal diary.

4. Don't ever say 'It's easy'. (It isn't.)

5. Don't ever say 'Why didn't you do it before?' (She was much too frightened.)

6. Don't pressurise her to be social. (It makes her feel worse.)

7. Don't pretend she looks good. (But when there is improvement, tell her.)

8. Don't flirt with other women. (It makes her feel even more inadequate.)

9. Don't get upset at tears. (In withdrawal, most people feel like occasionally turning on the taps!)

10. Understand when she feels tired. (She's probably not getting much sleep, and everything feels worse when one is weary.)

11. Do plan a special treat for when she's pill-free. (It makes her feel you are confident that there *will* be a tomorrow!)

12. Don't grumble at the food. (She can make all your favourites when she's not continually thinking about her symptoms.)

13. Don't get impatient when she's late again. (She gets even more tense when she rushes.)

14. Don't scold her when she leaves the car lights on! (She really can't remember everything, can she?)

15. Don't shout when she leaves the bath taps on! (Just turn them off and thank God you were there.)

16. Do consult her over family decisions. (She is no longer an uninterested zombie!)

17. Do let *her* choose the TV programmes. (She probably can't be bothered with educational stuff.)

18. Don't feel rejected if she's not affectionate. (Just wait—you won't know what's hit you!)

19. Do tell her you love her. (She'll be difficult to convince!)

20. Do tell her you'll love her even more when she can discuss something other than her pills and hasn't a one-track mind!

II

I DON'T TAKE TRANQUILLISERS—HOW CAN THEY AFFECT ME?

Even people who have never taken tranquillisers or sleeping pills, nor ever been associated with an addict, may be affected by them. With an estimated 3.5 million people hooked on tranquillisers in Britain, and approximately 500 million people worldwide, it would be hard not to come into contact with an addict in our day-to-day lives. So how can a person's addiction affect the passer-by, neighbour, friend, client, colleague, employer and so forth? You have read in previous chapters of how addicts can lose confidence, memory and self-esteem, and how they cannot accomplish the easiest of tasks or make the simplest decisions. They may even have owned up to being aggressive and argumentative. All these traits may affect the outsider.

DRIVING

Driving is one area where we may all come into contact with a tranquilliser addict. I often wonder when I'm a passenger in a car (I don't drive) which of the other motorists on the road took a sleeping pill the previous night and jumped into his or her vehicle the next morning. How can the person who went to sleep under sedation or was calmed down by a pill with his breakfast cereal that morning be fully alert and have the fast reactions necessary to be safe on the road? Remember, some of these drugs have a cumulative effect, and it can take up to 250 hours for some of the long-acting tranquillisers to be metabolised by the body.

Arabella Melville and Colin Johnson write that the likelihood of having an accident while driving on tranquillisers is increased by a factor of five.[49] I came across one ironic story of a man who had been driving while he was taking benzodiazepines. Eventually, he came off the drugs and started to lead a normal life. His driving licence expired and he applied for a new one, but was refused because he had come off the drugs without the permission of his GP. Of course, he is far safer on the roads today than when he was on drugs.

Even more worrying and much more dangerous is the person who drinks socially when taking tranquillisers. The tranquilliser user may only have one glass of wine or one pint of beer and be legally under the limit when she puts the key in the ignition of her car, but in fact she is dangerously over the limit when she mixes drink with drugs. As I have mentioned before, just 2mg of Valium is the equivalent of a glass of wine. So if a tranquilliser addict was on a therapeutic dose of 5mg of Valium three times daily it would be similar to drinking 7½ glasses of wine a day. The tranquilliser addict is already over the limit before she's even drunk a sip! The government is always warning us not to drink and drive. My motto is don't take tranquillisers and drive, and definitely don't take tranquillisers, drink and drive.

Some tranquilliser addicts do give up driving because they realise they haven't the reflexes or the control needed to be safe on the road. But others carry on, especially when they are suffering from agoraphobia and their car becomes an extension of their home. Keith was a chauffeur. He drove throughout the time he was coming off his drugs and suffering from withdrawal symptoms. If he gave up driving, he would have had to give up his livelihood, which he couldn't afford to do. But every journey was a death drive. On many occasions he would be driving along the motorway at 70 m.p.h. and suffer a huge panic attack. As he was a chauffeur he couldn't stop on the hard shoulder—he had to keep on driving. 'It was like an explosion. I thought I was going to die there and then. Horrendous fear overcame me. I got pins and needles right down to the bottom of my fingernails. And my legs and everything seemed to seize up. Afterwards I felt like jelly, just shaking. I also suffered from blurred vision. When that happened I got round it by trying to look above it. But it was all very frightening. I thought I was going to pass out. I kept thinking I must be near the kerb in case something happens.'

His wife describes what it was like being a passenger. 'I went in the car with him when he was in withdrawal. He stuck to the highway code dead on. We kept on the inside lane. Then when he wanted to overtake he would swing out in front of other cars and slide back again. He gripped the steering wheel and automatic change until his knuckles went white. He was petrified and I was a twitching nervous wreck.'

VIOLENCE AND CRIME

Can tranquillisers actually cause violence and crime?

As mentioned in Part Two, because tranquillisers can change our character so that we become more argumentative and aggressive, this may lead some people to crime. Some doctors have attributed the increase in baby-battering, wife-beating and grandma-bashing to the taking of tranquillisers.[50] Melville and Johnson write: 'It is possible that increased use of tranquillisers is actively contributing to the rising violence of the affluent countries. They have been shown to lead to violent outbreaks in much the same way as alcohol.'[51]

You have read in Part One how Paul confesses that he did indeed commit more crimes under the influence of a benzodiazepine drug because he lost all sense of reasoning. Tranquillisers gave him a couldn't-care-less attitude, so he would shoplift, steal credit cards and cars—even rob banks. He says: 'All reasoning goes out of the window, I thought to myself "Who gives a damn?" I'd take four tranquillisers and feel as high as a kite and I'd go out and do it [commit a crime].' Although he knew he was committing the crime, he was unable to think of the consequences.

Paul also found that when he was taking drugs he was more likely to get into fights. 'I never had a fight in my life until I went on tranquillisers, never. I'm too scared. I don't like fighting. I take tranquillisers and I don't care.' When he was in prison, and still on

tranquillisers, this aggressiveness came out. 'If somebody said something to me, like the prison officers getting on my back, I used to
have a go at them. I actually hit one of them and lost remission for it.'

   Maybe if people weren't on tranquillisers, society would be a safer
place in which to live.

AT WORK

It isn't that easy to detect the tranquilliser addict at work. Many
addicts have carried on working, some even in high-powered jobs,
without their colleagues or employers knowing about their
dependence.

   You may wonder how addicts can cope with decision-making,
people and pressure when they are suffering from the loss of their
concentration, memory, confidence and self-esteem, and all the
other side-effects of the drugs. The answer is that they become good
actors. They are so ashamed of needing a 'crutch' that they will do
anything to hide their addiction. But, of course, there is a price to
pay. The price is more pills.

   Pam, an assistant physiotherapist, explains how she coped with
work while she was on tranquillisers. 'I think the hardest part was
going to work and putting on this act. The physiotherapists
depended on me to cheer up the patients, they would say, "It's all
right, Pam's coming in today." I was the life and soul of the ward, but
inside I was dying, I was far worse than the patients. I would have to
hide in the toilet because I couldn't do my job when the panic attacks
came, then I would take a little bit extra to carry me through.'

   Margaret, a conference organiser, remembers: 'I was just a nightmare at work. I was trying to keep up this tremendous facade, being
called into management meetings and being absolutely sweating that
I was going to be asked for something—a spot decision or a
resumé—very quickly. I had to think on my feet and I knew I
couldn't do it.'

   Frank kept up his cover at work, but it was when he got home that
the strain had its effect. 'I just fell apart. I would just go upstairs and
lie down on the bed and collapse.'

   This act isn't only to do with the addicts' shame of being on the drugs—it's to do with protecting their jobs as well. Once their employer knows about their addiction, they know that their jobs may be threatened, or they may lose out on promotion. If they are seeking a position and they admit to taking or having taken drugs, they may not be chosen even if they are the ideal candidate for the job. A manager of a large firm confirms this by saying, 'It creates a barrier. The employer will think it's a problem he could well do without.'

Unfortunately, we may have difficulty getting a promotion or a good job when we are off our drugs, even though we have shown tremendous strength of character to overcome our dependence. Employers may still have little understanding of how our character can change, and of how much more alert we become once we are off drugs. Hopefully their attitude will change as the general public becomes more aware that a tranquilliser addict is not necessarily an addict for life.

IN SOCIETY

The average man in the street can be very unsympathetic to the tranquilliser addict, and usually they do not accept withdrawal as an illness. Harry found this out when his company started to fall behind in paying the bills. It wasn't because he was a bad businessman, but because he was ill. But no one, from the banks to his debtors, accepted this reason. They treated him in the same way as anyone who has bad debts to pay—there were, they said, no mitigating circumstances. He was threatened with imprisonment and his house was repossessed.

Even friends can turn their back on a tranquilliser addict. When Angela told her friends about her addiction to benzodiazepines, she found them very unsympathetic. 'I soon found out who were my friends and, most importantly, who weren't. I felt extremely abandoned. I was ignored. They were scared. They didn't know how to handle me. It was different when I had cancer, then everybody was supportive and everybody rallied around. But with tablets I was *persona non grata.*'

If society were to understand the problems of tranquilliser

addiction more, then maybe the tranquilliser addict would not be shunned and considered a second-class citizen. After all, it may have been the pressures of society that put us on the drugs in the first place. Trying to understand the problem of tranquilliser addiction should start in the GP's surgery, but Dr Betsy Ettore, Research Fellow at the Centre for Research on Drugs and Health Behaviour, London, warns: 'GPs have been resistant to changes and influences on the way they prescribe . . . that's why it is important that agencies like TRANX (UK) actually do continue, because at least they are generating public awareness of the problem.'

PART FIVE

LOOKING AHEAD

I

THE NEW ME

'Learning to walk again.'

THE SECOND STAGE OF RECOVERY

Now we are free of drugs—free of our 'crutch'. And so we enter into the second stage of our recovery—the period where we have to learn how to cope on our own. We have to regain our courage to face life and its problems. Our fears, anxieties and phobias may still be with us, but now we have to learn to deal with them. As our emotions begin to surface we have to learn to recognise and accept them without being afraid. In time, as our withdrawal symptoms become a thing of the past and our own 'coping mechanism' begins to work again, we should emerge as the 'new me': a person who is stronger and more confident. I am convinced that we all can find this inner strength and work towards this goal.

But *full* recovery does not happen overnight. Just as losing our coping mechanism was a very gradual process while we were on the drugs, so can regaining it happen extremely slowly. Sometimes we may not even realise that we are actually progressing and getting better. It can take up to one or maybe two years. That may sound like a lifetime, but that is how long it can take for the GABA, our own natural substance in the brain, to start working again. Even when we are having a 'bad day' we must look at it positively, and see it as part of the road to recovery.

However, recovery won't just happen. We have to work at it. It is a learning process. Just as a baby has to learn how to walk, so we have to teach ourselves how to cope with everything in life. Sometimes ex-addicts, at this stage in their recovery, come to me and tell me they can't walk or go out or do the shopping. They mentally and physically feel they cannot do these things. I tell them that they *can*, but they have to *want* to do them. You have to *want* to get better. It's the determination to get well that should get you there.

When you are low and feel you may not win through, think about the willpower of a baby learning how to walk. She'll take one step and fall down, but then she'll get up. She may attempt two steps the next time before she falls. She'll get up again and fall down, but she'll keep on trying until she can walk. And that is how we must be: we have to keep on persevering until we have recovered.

Dr Heather Ashton conducted a study of 50 patients who had been taking prescribed benzodiazepines regularly for 1 to 22 years and decided to come off. She then looked at how these patients were getting on when they had been off drugs for periods which ranged from ten months to three-and-a-half years.[52]

Grading	Definition	Number and percentage of patients
Excellent (fully recovered)	Minimal symptoms, leading a normal life, full-time job, no regular medication (may still be 'highly strung')	24 (48%)
Good (much better)	Some symptoms but able to lead normal life, full-time job	11 (22%)
Moderate (better)	Coping, but still with symptoms which interfere with life or require other drugs (e.g. beta-blockers, anti-depressants)	8 (16%)

Grading	Definition	Number and percentage of patients
Poor (no better)	Off benzodiazepines but still with multiple psychological symptoms and/or needing other psychotropic medication (e.g. antidepressants, sedative/hypnotics)	3 (6%)
Failed (relapsed, unable to withdraw)	Started benzodiazepines again after withdrawal, unable to withdraw, multiple symptoms still present	4 (8%)

This clearly shows that the majority of people do very well after benzodiazepine withdrawal, and the rate of relapse or failure to withdraw is very low. Dr Cosmo Hallstrom and Dr Mark Tattersall conducted a survey for TRANX (UK), and found that we had a 68 per cent success rate for clients who had withdrawn from all benzodiazepines nine months after contacting us.

THE LEARNING PROCESS

Learning to cope with fears and anxieties

Even when we have been off all our mood-altering drugs for some time, some of us may still be troubled with our fears, anxiety and phobias. They may not be so acute now, but they may be lingering within us. Now's the time to start to take control of them, so that they won't be in control of us.

This is how Vivian overcame her agoraphobia. 'For me the glory was to go to work on a bus, not in a cab. One day I felt especially strong, so I decided I was going to take the bus. It was the most ridiculous journey I've ever made because the bus broke down. It took me I don't know how long, and I was feeling "this is wonderful—I'm on a bus". Everyone else around me was tearing their hair out, but I was smiling to myself. That was my first journey. Now I can do anything. I still have to cling on to my boyfriend's arm when we go into a department store, but for somebody who wouldn't stick their nose out of the front door three months ago, I think it's wonderful.'

Like Liz, on page 64, Karen had a cleaning obsession. Although she has been off for two years, she admits that she still has this obsession from time to time, but she stresses, 'I'm learning to control it. On the drugs I had no control over it at all.' And Keith, who suffered hypochondria on the drugs and has been off for eleven and a half months, says, 'I'm much more relaxed about things now than I've ever been.'

Learning to cope with life

We are on our own. We haven't got that little pill to see us through any more. We have to learn how to cope with a temperamental boss, an active child, a heavy work load, a bad marriage, the shopping, dinner parties, birthdays and Christmas—in fact, anything that life throws at us. But we *can* learn to cope with these things because we are slowly becoming stronger, and more in control of ourselves.

Margaret, a working mother, off drugs for two years, describes how she copes. 'I work in town and I have to get back for the children when they come out of school. I used to think, "What if I start panicking, what if I can't do my work, what if I can't get back in time?" But now I say to myself, "I've done it all before, I've felt like this before, I *can* cope". It's wearing—physically exhausting when I feel like that, but the quicker I can get it under control the shorter it lasts—and it's lessening.'

Betty, off drugs for three years, now takes this attitude: 'I do get anxious, I do worry; but it doesn't mean to say I've got to take pills. What are they going to do? Even now I've been off for some time, I can never stop reminding myself that I could never have done that or this, or I never felt like that when I was on pills.'

Learning to cope with emotions

Now our body and mind are free of drugs, our natural emotions begin to come alive again. We experience the sensation of having feelings which we haven't had during our time on pills. We laugh. We cry. We love. We hate. Because we haven't had these emotions for such a long time, we find it hard to deal with them. We have to learn to accept them and not be afraid. Before, when we were on drugs and we experienced an emotion we didn't like, such as sadness, we would take a pill. But although we covered up sadness, we also covered up happiness. Now, we have all the emotions tumbling back—the ones we like and the ones we don't like. But they've all got to be embraced and dealt with.

Earlier I mentioned that my daughter Maira remembered what it was like for her when my emotions started to surface again. 'Although Mum was always there, at home, when she had come off she started to come alive. Then I thought what a shame it was that I had missed out on this. Missed out on seeing her like this during my childhood.'

Vivian lost the emotion of love and compassion for her child when she was on drugs, and she recalls how that precious feeling came back. 'I was cuddling my daughter one day, when this feeling came over me. It was the same feeling I had for her when she was born—a feeling of the wonderment about this little creature.' And Suzanne says this about her marriage: 'I was virtually on benzodiazepines all of my eighteen years of married life. I haven't shown much love. But my husband has stuck with me all the way through. Now our relationship is getting better and better. I have re-fallen in love with him.'

Sad emotions come back as well. Liz grieved for her grandfather's death for the first time fifteen years after he died.

Of course, as our emotions start to resurface we begin to react to situations again and make decisions, which we may have been unable to do on the drugs.

We become more confident

As we start to regain our confidence, we slowly begin to respect ourselves more and more. We look at our wants, our needs and our desires. People will not be able to manipulate us as they may have been able to do when we were on drugs. Now that our mind is clear, we can see what is happening. We will no longer put up with being the 'doormat' of society or of our family. Our new confidence is likely to be even greater than before we went on drugs: after all, having gone through the process of recovery we should be able to tackle anything.

'People used to give me crap, and I couldn't sort it out when I was on pills,' says Liz. 'I believe everyone has crap, everyone has rubbish in them. A lot of people can't deal with their own rubbish so if there's a tranquilliser addict around they'll dump it on them. I became the dumping ground for everyone else's rubbish. When I came off pills my ex-husband said something to me. I said, "That's crap, don't do that to me." He couldn't handle it. I said, "You can't do that to me any more, I'm no longer on pills."'

Vivian says, 'I have changed. I think that for myself, I've changed for the better; for other people—worse. I've always been a person who tried to please others and denied myself. Now I'm trying to please myself. I'm trying to lead a life that I want to lead. I'm listening to *me* and what I need. I think I've got a bit more selfish, so I think I'm nicer to myself but for other people I'm more difficult.'

As our mind opens we can think more clearly, as Sally found out. 'Over the months I could see things more clearly. I could see what I had done. Sometimes it wasn't such a good thing because I could see the terrible mistakes I had made in my life through the tablets. But I can't go back. There's no way I can get those years back.'

Self-confidence also shows in the way we dress. We take a pride in our appearance because we are proud of ourselves. When Betty was on drugs she didn't bother about her appearance. She would wear the same clothes every day. She'd wash them but wear them again. She didn't have any incentive to buy herself a new outfit. Now she is off drugs she is smartly dressed. Her job requires it—she runs her own catering company.

As our confidence increases, so does our efficiency. 'Karen now works for a nursing home,' says her husband, 'who reckon her to be one of their most efficient nurses. So she gets the pick of the jobs. It's a piece of cake to her now—so it should be because she is an intelligent person. But before when she was on tranquillisers she was reduced to the level of a sort of cabbage—everything was too complicated, too difficult.'

We become more understanding

An experience as dramatic as coming off and recovery will obviously leave its scars, but I have found it can also help the person to grow mentally. Of course, going through withdrawal and recovery may have been painful both emotionally and physically for us, but it has also been a time when we can look at ourselves and our life which surrounds us. Few people have time for this luxury—they are too busy trying to keep up with today's fast living to step back and reflect. But we have had time to stop and take note. We have learnt about our anxieties and vulnerabilities, and how to cope with them. We have realised our needs and our wants. And hopefully we have become strong enough to be able to change our life so that we may benefit from the experience.

Because we have had to confront and come to terms with our pains, we have become wiser and more understanding of others. With this knowledge we are able to view the world with greater compassion. We are more caring for the people with real problems, and most probably less tolerant of wingers. There is little we don't know about emotions and feelings, now. If life is an education, we have surely achieved the highest honours through a difficult but rewarding learning process.

THE LOST YEARS

In recovery we can learn to overcome our fears, phobias and anxieties. We can learn to be stronger, more confident and understanding. But there is one thing we can never get back, and that is the years passed in a haze on tranquillisers and/or sleeping pills—those lost years.

The following comments express the feelings of many addicts. For Betty, the time spent on drugs was 'as bad as going to prison. To me I have wasted eighteen years of my life.' For Liz, coming off was 'a bit like waking up and looking in the mirror, and feeling I had been asleep for twenty years. Can you imagine being nineteen years old and then losing your twenties and thirties? I'd aged twenty years. But I didn't know what had happened in all that time. My memory system had gone. Twenty years had been lost.' Pam said: 'When I look back on all those years I was on pills, I feel I have missed out on so much.'

Parents remark that they don't remember their children growing up. They may look at old photographs, but they can't remember the occasions. There are no stored memories to turn to. The years on drugs are a blank.

During the time we have been on benzodiazepines, we may have gone through life without emotions and events registering. It's as if our mind has been locked in a time-capsule. When we come off we may find that our emotions haven't developed with age. We are older, our bodies are older, but our emotions are still where they were when we went on pills. Daniel went on tranquillisers when he was 16 years old, and came off at the age of 32. 'I'm getting back to dating girls. It's weird because in some ways I'm like a teenager now,' he says.

WE CAN'T BLAME THE PILLS FOREVER—OR CAN WE?

By the second year off all mood-altering drugs we should be feeling reasonably well and back to normal, although symptoms can still resurface occasionally. However, Dr David Marjot believes that withdrawal symptoms may 'ebb and flow' for a lifetime in a diminishing fashion.

We may never scientifically know whether our bodies are totally free of drugs. It may be impossible to detect. After a period of time from coming off benzodiazepines, doctors are unable to measure the level of the drug in our blood, but that does not mean it is not there. Some of it has dissolved in the fatty tissues in our body—and the brain has a lot of fatty tissues.[53]

There is also the point that we can still be extremely vulnerable to any stresses (environmental or emotional) for a very long time, because we conceive our emotions in the 'raw'. Therefore, our own anxiety symptoms are often accentuated, making them feel identical to withdrawal symptoms.

However, some people use withdrawal symptoms to hide behind, just as they hid behind drugs. They use it as an excuse. As Keith said to me, 'Withdrawal is fantastic because you can blame everything on it.'

But now it is time to face life and your problems. It is my personal opinion that if by the second year of recovery you still feel you have *severe* symptoms of anxiety and/or depression and you feel you cannot cope with them, either because of things that have happened in the past or because of what is happening to you now, then you should seek counselling. That way you can talk your problems through and get to the *cause* of your symptoms, instead of pushing them away and covering them up with drugs.

WILL YOUR FAMILY ADJUST TO THE 'NEW YOU'?

How do your partner and family cope with your changed personality? Do they accept this new confident, self-assured, self-assertive, clear-thinking person? You may think that they will be sure to like the 'new you'. But will they?

One of the reasons why some people go on drugs is because of a bad marital relationship. Your partner may like you to be subservient and submissive. Now that you are more confident you won't accept things as easily—you won't be trodden on any more. So your partner's attitude will have to change; but does your partner really *want* this change?

One survey found that it was difficult for families to re-adjust to the 'new you'. Indeed, in some instances a relationship between partner and addict might only have survived because the addict was on pills and had a problem. The partner felt more comfortable or more secure that way.[54]

Chola and Ula live in Nigeria, where the wife is still very much under the husband's thumb. But when Chola came off her mood-altering drugs, she started to speak her mind. Her behaviour went against her upbringing and what was socially expected of her. This, of course, was very bewildering and difficult to accept for both of them.

Even if your partner and family want you to be drug-free and are willing to accept your changed personality, it may take them a while to re-adjust. 'The hardest thing to adjust to when Frank came off,' says Jenny, 'was not being there with him all the time. I had to give him space to do his things, and I found that so difficult. I would worry all the time when he went out. If he was just five minutes late home from work I was like the inquisition when he came in. Where have you been? What have you been doing? Why have you been there? Because he had tried to commit suicide when he was on the drugs, I couldn't let go—that fear stayed with me for a long time. Also, I had got so used to being with him, doing everything for him all the time and taking him places, that when he wanted to go off and do things by himself, I felt hurt that he didn't need me as much.'

IS IT WORTH IT?

Recovery may not be easy to get through, but it is definitely better than a life on drugs. Here are the benefits and drawbacks of being drug-free.

Benefits

More confident
More in control
Fitter
Eyes look brighter
Improved vision
Less irritable
Less aggressive
Less moody
Less depressed
Think more clearly
Work more effectively
More patience
Better sex life
No need to carry pills around
Appreciate life around you
Wake up brighter in the morning
Feel much fitter and live longer

Save money
Improved family and personal relationships
More socialising

Drawbacks

Temptation to smoke more or eat sweets
Temptation to drink alcohol
Need to learn to cope with tensions and anxieties
Have to face life's problems without 'crutches'
Families and friends have to re-adjust to your new confidence
Have to avoid most sedatives and painkillers if medically possible.

II

AM I GOING TO BE AFFECTED FOR THE REST OF MY LIFE?

'What the drugs did to me inwardly—no one could have done more damage if they had cut me up with a knife.'

Frank

As you have read, the scars of tranquilliser addiction and the withdrawal symptoms may take a long time to heal—both emotionally and physically. And there may be a possibility that the drug could take a lifetime to leave our body.

Now that we have been addicted and have gone through withdrawal, there are, in my experience, certain risks which we run.

BANNED FROM BENZODIAZEPINES

Just as an alcoholic cannot drink another glass of spirits, wine or beer, so the tranquilliser addict should, in my opinion, avoid taking other mood-altering drugs when possible, because they may spark off the craving and dependency again.

But unlike the alcoholic, who can avoid his drink, the tranquilliser addict may find it more difficult to avoid taking benzodiazepines again. For instance, we may have an operation, and the 'pre-med' before the anaesthetic can be a shot of benzodiazepines.

So what are the consequences if we have to have a benzodiazepine injection? We found at TRANX that ex-addicts who have taken the 'pre-med' before they have undergone an operation have experienced withdrawal symptoms for a short period of time, and some of them experienced their craving for the drug again. Dr Marjot was concerned about this, but what he found most worrying was the way ex-tranquilliser addicts were treated by the hospital staff. The ex-addicts were given little sympathy and were treated very much like second-class citizens, when all they were trying to ensure was that their treatment in hospital did not impair their recovery.

So what can we do when we are faced with having an operation? We cannot avoid having the operation, but we may be able to avoid having the 'pre-med' (the benzodiazepine injection). That does not mean we will be awake during the operation! The 'pre-med' is not the anaesthetic—it is simply the injection that makes you sleepy before you go down to the operating theatre. Some people can become very nervous about having an operation, and in that case having the 'pre-med' to calm them down may be necessary. But others may not worry about going down to the operating theatre fully awake. So we now have the choice of whether we let our bodies have the shock of a benzodiazepine injection (clients have reported severe muscle spasms) or the shock of having an anaesthetic without any sedation. Dr Bhatt suggests that the shock to the body of an operation is not as great as it is made out to be, and that there are alternatives to benzodiazepines where operations are concerned. Remember: we have the choice. We don't have to consent to the 'pre-med'.

When I had my hysterectomy I didn't consent to having the 'pre-med' or post-operative morphine or strong painkillers. I was totally relaxed when I went down to the operating theatre, and the operation was a success. But the moment I woke up from the anaesthetic I was fully awake and completely aware of the excruciating pain. As I was lying in bed in agony, the women who had had the same operation but with all the usual injections were still asleep, totally unaware of what had happened to them. But I had decided I would prefer the pain of the operation to the pain of withdrawal symptoms. That had been my choice. Of course, ideally we should avoid all sedating drugs where possible, though some may be necessary for our treatment, such as beta-blockers, which are prescribed for high blood pressure. But any drug that is sedating can lead to dependence.

Let's take a look at these drugs. The pharmaceutical industry will always produce other sedating drugs to help us.

One such group of drugs is antidepressants. Some doctors find antidepressants helpful in withdrawal, and they say that their patients are successful in coming off benzodiazepines when they take this drug. But what happens when the patient comes off antidepressants? I have found that antidepressants keep the withdrawal symptoms of the benzodiazepines, and therefore recovery, at bay, and we will only feel the full withdrawal effect when we are off both benzodiazepines and antidepressants. However, as mentioned on page 60, in some *very* severe cases antidepressants may be unavoidable.

The reason why we cannot take certain drugs any more isn't because we have become anti-drug, but because our bodies seem to have become hypersensitive and hyper-responsive to them. Dr Heather Ashton, although she cannot give a chemical reason why we develop adverse reactions to other drugs, suggests that as the GABA in the brain affects nearly every system in our body, it is perhaps not surprising that our bodies' response to drugs may be affected too.

But you don't need me to tell you to become more cautious when accepting prescribed drugs from your doctor. Most ex-tranquilliser addicts no longer take their doctor's word as gospel. They have suffered too much and have become more aware of the side-effects of drugs. 'Now if the doctor says I've got something, even an ingrowing toenail, I'd get a second opinion,' says Frank. Fortunately some doctors are learning to become more understanding of our problem and to be more explicit when prescribing drugs to their patients. Betty's doctor told her when she had recovered: 'I'll never write out a prescription for you again without explaining what I'm giving you.' Let's hope that other doctors follow this pattern with all their patients.

When we are cutting down and in recovery, we should not have an alcoholic drink, even on a social occasion, for some time. The glass of wine, pint of beer or tot of spirit should be left well alone, especially in the first year of coming off. You already know that alcohol is mood-altering (see page 114), therefore by drinking you would simply be exchanging one drug for another. Some ex-tranquilliser addicts, who have been off for longer than a year, have taken the occasional drink and reported that they felt unwell after it. And remember Tim, who had been off tranquillisers for over a year when he decided to drink alcohol socially with his friends? He began to suffer from anxiety and panic attacks again. Of course, he believed that his original anxiety problem had come back, and didn't consider that alcohol might be the cause. He went to his doctor who decided that the best treatment was benzodiazepines, and so Tim started on the cycle of addiction all over again.

III

COPING WITH STRESS—
WITHOUT PILLS

You have recovered. Congratulations!

But life is still plagued with all kinds of stress and anxiety. Below are ways of dealing with them successfully without tranquillisers.

TALKING

Talk. Talk. Talk. Talking can be one of the best remedies for relieving stress and anxiety. The old saying is 'a problem shared is a problem halved', and I firmly believe that. When you are upset or worried about a situation, find yourself someone who can be a good listening ear. He or she doesn't have to be a professional counsellor, just anyone—partner, friend or relative—on whom you can off-load, and who would be willing to share your problems and thoughts. Although the person needn't have training, they must be prepared to listen, and mustn't insist on giving you advice: if you are to help yourself, it is important that you should work out your own solutions to your own problems. By explaining your problems to someone, you will find you will begin to sort them out in your own mind. Time and time again, clients have said to me: 'If only I had talked to someone, my anxiety would have been all over so much sooner. And if only I had talked to someone when I first went to the doctor, I never would have needed those nasty little pills to help me through.' Karen's husband now realises that all Karen needed was someone to listen to her problems at the time. 'Karen didn't like the way her life was going,' he says. 'She was mixed-up and upset. And because she was upset she was given pills when really she needed to sort out her life.'

Today, psychiatrists and doctors are becoming more and more aware that counselling can be more effective in the treatment of anxiety than drugs. A trial was conducted in Oxford in which half the patients were given benzodiazepines to treat their anxiety and the other half had a brief chat to their doctor about their worries. Within one month depression had dropped to 40 per cent in both groups, and by the end of seven months it had dropped to 30 per cent. The doctors came to the conclusion that for patients with mild or moderate anxiety, the best treatment is likely to be brief counselling provided by the general practitioner or by another professional working in the practice.[55]

So the next time you have a worry, *talk* to someone about it. You will see your problem much more clearly afterwards, and feel much better for it.

RELAXATION

The ability to relax is a wonderful gift to have—and anyone can learn the technique. There is nothing magical or mystical about it, but once you have learnt how to relax, you are equipped with a natural safety valve for when life gets too stressful.

Relaxation isn't simply taking a nap. It can help you in many ways. It can help you to cope naturally with stress, and so can ease stress-related disorders. It can help to alleviate aches and pains, it can help you avoid unnecessary fatigue, and it can make personal relationships easier, give feelings of well-being, and aid restorative sleep.[56]

Make time for your relaxation: it is not a self-indulgence, for it can help you to keep healthy, both physically and mentally.

THE RELAXATION TECHNIQUE
(Courtesy of Monica Burton, Dipl. THP, SRN, MSAPP)

Preparation Sit in a comfortable chair or, better still, lie down. Choose a warm quiet room when you are not too tired and where you will not be interrupted.

If you are sitting, take off your shoes, uncross your legs, and rest your arms along the arms of the chair.

If you are lying down, lie on your back, with your arms at your sides.

Close your eyes and be aware of your body. Notice how you are breathing and where the muscular tensions in your body are. Make sure you are comfortable.

Breathing Start to breathe slowly and deeply, expanding your chest as you breathe in, then raising your rib cage to let more air in, until your lungs are filled right to the top. Hold your breath for a couple of seconds and then breathe out slowly, allowing your rib cage and abdominal muscles to relax, and empty your lungs completely. Do not strain: with practice it will become much easier.

Keep this slow, deep rhythmic breathing going throughout your relaxation session.

Relaxation After you have got your breathing pattern established, start the following sequence.

1. Curl your toes hard and press your feet down.
Tense up on an 'in' breath, hold your breath for ten seconds while you keep your muscles tense, then relax and breathe out at the same time.

2. Press your heels down and hold your feet up.
Tense up on an 'in' breath, hold your breath for ten seconds; relax on an 'out' breath.

3. Tense your calf muscles.
Tense up on an 'in' breath, hold for ten seconds; relax on an 'out' breath.

4. Tense your thigh muscles, straightening your knees and making your legs stiff.
Tense up on an 'in' breath, hold for ten seconds; relax on an 'out' breath.

5. Make your buttocks tight.
Tense up on an 'in' breath, hold for ten seconds; relax on an 'out' breath.

6. Tense your abdomen as if to receive a punch.
Tense up on an 'in' breath, hold for ten seconds; relax on an 'out' breath.

7. Bend your elbows and tense the muscles of your arms.
Tense up on an 'in' breath, hold for ten seconds; relax on an 'out' breath.

8. Hunch your shoulders and press your head back into the cushions.
Tense up on an 'in' breath, hold for ten seconds, relax on an 'out' breath.

9. Close your jaws, frown and screw up your eyes really tight.
Tense up on an 'in' breath, hold for ten seconds; relax on an 'out' breath.

10. Tense all your muscles together.
Tense up on an 'in' breath, hold for ten seconds; relax on an 'out' breath.

Remember to breathe deeply, and be aware when you relax of the feeling of physical well-being and heaviness spreading through your body.

After you have been through the whole sequence from 1 to 10, keep breathing slowly and deeply and imagine a white rose on a black background. Try to 'see' the rose as clearly as possible, concentrating your attention on it for 30 seconds. Do not hold your breath during this time, but continue to breathe as you have been doing.

After this, go on to visualise anything else that is pleasant to you, or give yourself the instructions that when you open your eyes you will be perfectly relaxed and alert.

Then count to three before opening your eyes.

BREATHING

Shallow breathing or over-breathing (hyperventilating) is very common in withdrawal. Many of our symptoms could be relieved if we simply breathed properly, especially when we are having panic attacks. Taking deep breaths can calm us down, naturally.

As with relaxation, breathing correctly can be learnt. Practise this commonly used abdominal exercise as often as you can, so that it becomes second nature to you. Then you will be able to turn to it when you are feeling anxious, or when you feel a panic attack is coming on.

Abdominal breathing

You can do abdominal breathing in any position—standing up, lying down or sitting. If you need to use this breathing technique when you are out, even if you are in a crowded room, no one need notice you doing it.

However, if you are at home and you want to use your breathing technique, lying on your back is a good position. So, lie down. Make sure you are warm and comfortable. Have the knees bent to relax the lower back, and place the soles of the feet on the floor just under the knees. Concentrate on the abdominal or tummy area, and relax that area.

1. Place the right hand just below the rib cage, and the left hand just below the right hand. Do not apply any pressure with either hand, they are there purely as a reminder of where to direct the attention.

2. Now concentrate on the area under the right hand. Start with a deep exhalation, the 'out' breath, breathing through the nose. Pull the abdomen in gently, taking it back towards the spine as far as you can, to empty the lungs as much as possible. (They can never be completely empty.)

3. Then just allow the inhalation, the 'in' breath, to follow. Be aware of the rise and fall of the area beneath the right hand. Do guard against bloating the abdomen.

4. Then relax the arms to the sides and revert to normal breathing.

HEALTHY EATING

In recovery it is essential to eat a well-balanced diet. I found when I was in the last stage that I wanted to eat 'healthy' foods because it gave me a feeling that I was cleansing my body. Some foods may actually help recovery along and other foods may hinder it.

Foods to eat

Foods rich in protein, such as milk, cheese, eggs, fish, soya beans, wheat germ and peanuts, can actually help with panic attacks. I always had a piece of cheese nearby for when I felt a panic attack coming on.

Nuts, whole grains, dried beans and kelp contain the mineral magnesium, which can help fight depression.

Bananas contain tryptophan, which is a natural antidepressant.

Honey clears the liver.

Foods to avoid

Refined carbohydrates, such as sugar, chocolate, sweets, white bread, white flour, cakes and biscuits, have little nutritive value and contain hardly any roughage. You may develop a 'sweet tooth' in early recovery, but it is better to avoid refined sweet food. I found that when I ate a lot of sweets it increased my sugar level and therefore stimulated panic attacks.

Caffeine, found in chocolate, coffee, tea and cola, stimulates the central nervous system and the production of adrenaline, and therefore can stimulate panics.

Professor Malcolm Lader carried out a study of people suffering from anxiety. He cut out all their caffeine intake, and a quarter of the patients improved. He believes that caffeine can make the mildly anxious person more anxious, and make the anxious person panic.[57] I certainly found when I stopped drinking coffee and tea that my anxiety reduced.

RECREATION

Take up a sport or hobby. Activities can really help you, both in recovery and afterwards. Choose something you enjoy doing and try to keep to a regular routine—an hour every day if you can. Different activities work different areas of the body and mind. Sports such as swimming, jogging and walking can get rid of your surplus adrenaline. Yoga teaches you the art of relaxation and breathing while gently stretching your body. A hobby such as painting can take your mind off your symptoms, and stop you falling into the 'poor-little-old-me' syndrome.

IV

LOOK AT US NOW

You *can* get better. You can have a new life without mood-altering drugs. This table of the men and women whom you have read about in this book tells you what they are doing today.

	Years on drugs	Years off drugs	Occupation now
Liz	16	4	Works in theatre box office
June	30	2	Running her husband's financial business since his death
Frank	7	4	Continued to work in the fashion business throughout his withdrawal
Margaret	15	3	Conference organiser and is about to take a degree course
Angela	30	1 month	Taking a counselling course and childminding
Martin	2	1	Running his own company full time again
Pam	16	1	Returned to her previous job as an assistant occupational therapist

	Years on drugs	Years off drugs	Occupation now
Daniel	9	5 months	Library assistant
Diana	5	2	Started a new career in public relations, having worked for TRANX as a counsellor
Sally	25	2	Helps her husband in his business and is a part-time shop assistant
Audrey	15	11 months	Returned to her previous job as teacher in adult education
Vivian	3	1	PA for major company
Betty	18	7	Runs successful catering company with other ex-addicts
Gloria	11	6	Returned to her job as a qualified nanny
Keith	12	1	Continued to work as a chauffeur right through his withdrawal
Karen	9	4	Returned to nursing
Tim	7	3	Withdrawal changed his career—now he prefers to work outdoors clearing trees and travelling
Annette	18	1	Returned to working in Social Services
Harry	5	2	Started up in the fashion business again
Chola	8	3	Continued working as a nurse in an operating theatre right through withdrawal
Suzanne	15	2	Housewife
Doris	9	1	Housewife
Nickie	7	1	Teaching Spanish

PART SIX

TRANX (UK)

TRANX (UK)—
THE SELF-HELP GROUP

TRANX have no scientific evidence but they have the evidence of experience.
Dr David Marjot

It was January 1982. I had survived three weeks without sleeping pills or tranquillisers. I wandered around the drab wards of the Drug Dependency Unit, my vision so blurred that I could hardly see where I was going. As I walked, the walls seemed to swell up on me, making me feel giddy. And the feeling of a tight band around my head, which had come very soon after I had taken my last crumb, was still there. Sitting down gave me little relief—in fact it was more embarrassing, because wherever I sat I left a damp patch where I had been incontinent. And yet with all this pain I knew I was lucky. I was in a Drug Dependency Unit being helped, and I was determined to get better.

But I felt very much on my own. Out of the forty patients in the Unit I was the only one coming off tranquillisers and sleeping pills. All the rest were either alcoholics or hard drug addicts. The staff didn't know how to treat me—they had never met a tranquilliser addict before. At first they mocked me, but then as they saw how ill I became, they slowly began to sympathise.

When we sat in therapy groups, the staff said to me: 'Joan, whenever we mention the words alcohol or hard drugs, you should replace them with tranquillisers.' So I did. But no matter how they tried to include me, I always felt I was the odd one out. I began to think of all the other people hooked on benzodiazepines. I knew I couldn't be the only one. But where did all the other tranquilliser addicts go for help? They didn't come to the Drug Dependency Unit because I was the only one there, and the first one to be admitted. I wondered if the other addicts even knew they had a problem.

After six weeks I was discharged. I was far from well. I had been told by the doctors on my departure that my recovery might take a year. I was frightened, and I didn't want to face the pain I was going through all on my own. But where could I go for help? The only place I could think of was an alcoholics' recovery agency. After all, the staff in hospital had always told me to replace the word alcohol with tranquilliser. But when I went along to the group, they turned me away. I was a tranquilliser addict, not an alcoholic. I was different. I was on my own.

During those early weeks I was suffering from complete exhaustion and yet I couldn't sleep, and the pressure in my head went on and on, never letting up. I went to my doctor and asked for a sickness certificate to give me time to recover, but he refused. He didn't believe I could be ill from coming off tranquillisers.

As I had four children to support, I had no alternative but to go back to work as a secretary. I needed the money. As I sat at my desk in the office trying to type I was paranoid—I thought the other staff were talking about me. And when I took dictation from my boss, I felt as if he was talking to someone over my shoulder—it was as if I were unreal.

For months I suffered withdrawal on my own, with no one to help me, no one to reassure me, and no one to be there for me. But somehow I believed in myself. Somehow, through the pain, I knew I would get better. Somehow I knew that all my symptoms were because of the pills, and not because of me. And in the back of my mind I kept wondering who else was suffering, and who they were turning to for help.

The insomnia was brutal. I would lie awake in the dark, exhausted from the day and the pains of withdrawal, wishing my body and mind would fall into a warm gentle slumber—but it refused. For hours I'd listen to the clock ticking until the dawn chorus broke the stillness. Morning was approaching, and another night had been spent in torment instead of sleep. Some nights I'd get up and potter around the house, even though I ached with exhaustion.

The sleeplessness went on for months and months. Then one night I slept. For the first time in seventeen years I slept naturally—without pills. This simple, normal function was a marvel to me. I felt refreshed and alive. As I walked to work that morning everything seemed new—the shops, streets and trees, as if I was seeing them for the first time. Instead of the life around me going on in a haze or a muddle, I noticed what was happening: the people and what they were wearing, the shops and what they were selling, even the buildings took on a new dimension.

As I passed through the town centre, a bronze plaque caught my eye. Engraved on it were the words 'Community Health Council.' I stopped and stared at this well-polished plaque, and wondered if the Community Health Council knew that there was a tranquilliser problem. I decided to investigate.

I entered the building and was directed to their office.

'Can I help?' asked a neatly dressed woman.

'I do hope so.'

I told her my story, and that I believed that there were thousands of people like me who needed help. She smiled condescendingly.

'There isn't a tranquilliser problem in this area.'

'Of course there is,' I snapped. 'What makes you think the people around here don't take pills? Why are they so special?'

'I've told you there isn't a problem here,' she insisted in a controlled voice.

'Shall we see?' I contested. 'If I tell my story to the newspaper, will you be willing to monitor the calls for me?'

'Okay. I'll do that for you. But you're wasting your time.'

I left her office furious at her naivety. How could someone working for the Community Health Council not know and not be prepared to accept the possibility that there might be many people in the area hooked on tranquillisers? When I got home that evening, I sat at my typewriter and poured out my story on paper. The next day I took it to the local newspaper. The editor read my article and told me he would print it.

That Thursday I bought a copy of the newspaper, but the article wasn't in it. It wasn't in the following week or the week after that. I quite gave up on it ever appearing, but a few months later, just as I was leaving for work, the telephone rang.

'I've just read your story about your addiction to tranquillisers,' said a woman's voice.

'What story?' I was confused.

'In the newspaper.'

'It's finally come out? Has it?'

'It was as if you were talking about me. But I'm still hooked on those drugs.'

I listened patiently and sympathetically to her story—how her life was ruled by her pills, the illnesses she was suffering from, and how she wanted to give up but couldn't. Her story showed a startling resemblance to my own. I took her name and address and told her I would contact her.

No sooner had I replaced the receiver than the telephone rang again. This time it was a man's voice. He too had read my article in the newspaper, and was desperate to find help.

And so it carried on for the rest of the week. From the moment I arrived home from work until I went to bed I received call after call from tranquilliser addicts wanting to tell me their story. I listened and tried to help every one of them. I took each caller's telephone number and told them I would get back to them. My list of tranquilliser addicts grew longer and longer. By the end of the week I was tired but determined to do something about the problem. Then just as I was going to bed, at midnight, the telephone rang again.

'At last I've got through to you, Joan.' It was the woman from the Community Health Council.

'I'm sorry—the line's been busy with tranquilliser addicts from this area,' I said.

'I know. I've monitored over fifty calls,' she said. 'The office has been in a turmoil with all the extra work it's created.'

'I did tell you tranquilliser addiction was a problem.'

'I should have believed you, but how was I to know?'

I went to bed that night and slept soundly, knowing I was right. What I had suspected for many months, was a fact—there was a tranquilliser addiction problem. And it seemed that the only person who would do anything about it was me.

I decided to start a group in my front room. Out of the fifty tranquilliser users who telephoned me, fifteen came to the meeting. They all experienced an overwhelming relief to be among other tranquilliser users, and in a way were thankful that they weren't alone with their problem. We exchanged our experiences of withdrawal symptoms, doctors, psychiatrists, partners and events. By the end of the evening we decided to meet on a weekly basis.

The group grew and grew, and eventually I realised that I could no longer hold the meetings in my front room. I went to the Social Services, who offered me a room at the back of a scout hut for a small fee. A few months later the *Guardian* picked up on the story. As a result, six hundred letters from all over the country came flooding through my letter box. Letters of desperation, of fear, of grief and of panic all had to be answered. When I arrived home from work I got down to typing my replies, sometimes working into the small hours of the morning until every letter was answered. Suddenly my local group had turned nationwide.

The weekly group meeting was also quickly developing. I now needed to devote all my time to tranquilliser addiction. I decided there was no option but to give up my job as a legal secretary. My friends tried to dissuade me—I was giving up a well-paid job and I needed the money because I was still supporting my four children. But I was determined to let the public know what was going on with tranquillisers.

The first step was to get funding. Clutching my six hundred letters I went to the head office of the Department of Health and Social Security. They listened to me, but told me that in order to get funding I had to have charitable status, and for that I needed an executive committee. Only then could they consider my case. I came out of that meeting charged with enthusiasm and hope. I could actually visualise my wish of helping other tranquilliser users coming true. I didn't know how to form an executive committee, how to get charitable status or who to ask, but I had enough drive to find out.

I approached doctors, some contacts I had in the probation service and social workers—in fact anyone who I thought might be prepared to sit on my executive committee. The next step was to form a medical advisory panel of sympathetic doctors and psychiatrists. This wasn't so difficult, as the publicity had aroused interest from people in the medical profession as well as from sufferers.

Now the organisation needed a name. At one of the early executive committee meetings we decided to call it TRANX (Tranquilliser, Recovery and New Existence). A logo was needed too. One of the addicts came up with the idea of a hand in chains holding a torch, representing the choice between a life shackled by tranquillisers and freedom from drugs.

A few months later TRANX was featured on Esther Rantzen's *That's Life* television programme. That week, when I opened the weekly meeting in the scout hut, there wasn't the usual twenty or so tranquilliser users: it was jam-packed with over a hundred people. I divided everyone into groups with some of my established clients as leaders. Everyone was talking about their addiction and their problems. It was as if the tranquilliser user had come out of the cupboard. I realised then where my strength lay. These addicts didn't look to me for my knowledge—I had very little then, only what I had learnt from my own experience. They didn't come for my track record of getting people better, as I had only just begun. The addicts came because they could identify with me. At the end of the meeting one woman came up to me and said, 'When I see how you are, I know I can get off tranquillisers too.'

From that meeting I made it my philosophy that, if TRANX was going to grow, I would only employ people who were ex-addicts. I realised that to understand withdrawal *fully* and to be able to sympathise with the sufferer, you needed to have lived through it. Over the years we came up with a motto which sums up my feelings about the organisation: 'We've been there, look at us now.'

The response to the *That's Life* programme had also created a pile of work. I was working from early morning until late at night replying to letters and dealing with clients on the telephone—and I was still suffering from panic attacks myself! One night I created the world's first slow reduction charts for the withdrawal from benzodiazepines. Apart from a few modifications I still use these charts today, and they are now used worldwide by doctors and other agencies. They are given on pages 105–7.

Exactly a year after I started my first group, in December 1983, I was given £89,000 by the Department of Health and Social Security to run the self-help group for a period of three years and in that same month the organisation attained charitable status. I moved TRANX out of my front room and the scout hut into a local cottage, which became our offices and meeting place. There I set up the world's first tranquilliser telephone helpline, and four ex-tranquilliser users and I took calls of desperation from tranquilliser addicts all through the day.

The telephone helpline put us in touch with so many more addicts. The caller could live in Notting Hill Gate or Nottingham and still have the comfort of talking to someone who knew how she felt, who knew what it took to make the call, who knew what it felt like to feel depressed, panicky or in constant fear. We were there when she needed us—she didn't have to wait for an appointment or a letter, but could talk about her withdrawal when she was going through it. It was instant help.

'When I finally got through to TRANX on the telephone,' said Suzanne, 'they took away the uncertainty. They told me how much I could cut down at a time and how often. They explained every symptom and every side-effect. Not only did they explain it so that I stopped being scared of it, but I knew they had done it themselves, so they *knew*. It is only someone who has done it who really knows how it is to be that scared.'

For some addicts, the telephone helpline was one of the main 'safety nets' that got them through withdrawal. Even as TRANX grew, and offered other facilities, the telephone helpline became an integral part of coming off for many addicts. 'I leaned on TRANX a lot when I first started to cut down,' said Angela. 'Some days I phoned them once or twice, other days I didn't need to. But the important thing for me was that I knew they were there. They were only as far away as the end of the phone.'

Liz was another perpetual telephone caller through her withdrawal. She would phone again and again. 'I would get on the phone to TRANX and after they had finished talking I would say, "You've said this to me before, haven't you?" They said, "Yes." My brain wouldn't retain the good stuff, it wouldn't retain the reassurance, the confirmation that I should get better. I could have reassurance one minute and next I'd be climbing the walls saying, "I'm not going to make this, I need pills."'

As with any success story, other people wanted to jump on the bandwagon. Groups totally independent of TRANX started to use our name and our publicity for their own benefit. So, to distinguish us from other developing tranquilliser groups, on 29 April 1986 we became a company limited by guarantee, under the name of TRANX (UK).

Publicity grew. I was interviewed on the radio, television and in the press, spreading the word about tranquilliser addiction, and about how I could help sufferers have a new life without pills. As more and more tranquilliser addicts realised they could be helped, TRANX outgrew the small cottage. We moved to larger premises in the area, and offered more telephone helplines as now the calls were coming in at a rate of 2000 a month. We also offered individual therapy as well as the group sessions. I had a staff of ten, some of whom were part-time.

Every week thirty to forty people crammed themselves into our small meeting room for the group sessions. People sat on the floor, spilled out of the door, stood anywhere in earshot so that they could be with us. Knowing they were not the only ones feeling ill was one step towards their recovery. Of course, it didn't relieve their pain, but it helped to relieve the worry and anxiety. It gave them the reassurance that they were not terminally ill or going mad. They saw and heard with their own eyes and ears. 'I would have thought I was mentally ill, if someone hadn't said to me "I felt like that",' said Betty, one night after the meeting.

It was this great sense of identification that was so important to the addict when trying to come off her pills. 'June's big benefit,' said John, 'was her group therapy at TRANX. We used to go together and the things that were essentially June's problems proved to be the problems of all the people in the group. June would have palpitations one week and somebody would have had them the previous week. She would have breathlessness and other people would have been like that before. Everything June suffered, other people had suffered or were suffering or were likely to suffer, so seeing this made her realise that her problems were standard withdrawal. I found that very helpful too, because it became apparent that as we were getting through these various stages of withdrawal, we were making some progress. Because I was encouraged, I could encourage her to carry on with it in order to see things through. That was, I think, the lesson that TRANX taught us.'

Identifying with other sufferers was beneficial, but sometimes it went too far. Some clients who had just got over a particularly bad withdrawal symptom delighted in telling 'horror stories'. And on other occasions the withdrawal symptoms were 'catching'! The next day, after the session, some clients rang up suffering from the symptoms discussed at the meetings—though, of course, the symptom was possibly psychosomatic. 'If I was feeling rough,' said Margaret, 'the only hope I got was by looking at people who had got better and listening to them speak. If they could do it, so could I. But hearing other people's symptoms made me think if that can happen to her, it can happen to me. I just didn't have the strength of character to say no: it isn't going to happen to me.'

Apart from offering help for the tranquilliser addict, the group meetings gave support to the partner and family, the unknown sufferers. We became their extended family, and a place where the partners could be themselves, and not have to put on a brave face. They were given an insight into the tranquilliser problem. 'Before I went to TRANX,' explained one husband, 'I used to say to my wife, "Oh, you'll be all right, take another pill." I was so ignorant. And then when she was feeling depressed I used to say, "Why don't you buck yourself up?" We'd have rows—the marriage was on tenter-hooks at the time. If I'd known then what TRANX taught me, my marriage wouldn't have gone that way.'

And just as TRANX offered identification for the client, so it offered identification for the partner. Husbands, wives and children saw that they were not alone, that their relationship wasn't unique, and that other families were suffering in the same way. Most importantly, they saw that other families had survived. One partner turned to me in a group meeting and said, 'Now I can see a light at the end of the tunnel. You've given me hope.'

John felt that he not only learnt about withdrawal at the group session, but also about humanity. 'I found a great deal of sympathy for other people, which I might not have had if I hadn't have been to TRANX group therapies. Those sessions taught me a lot, especially about humanity. People there were really suffering through no fault of their own, and were bearing it with courage and with intelligence. I think I learned a lot from that. People there didn't have a lot of money, didn't have a lot of reward in their lives and they were prepared to take the problem and deal with it. I was very impressed with that, very impressed.'

Some clients needed individual counselling, which I gave later on in their recovery. These one-to-ones helped the client to look at any personal, emotional or environmental problems they might have had or might still have. But I was always aware during the sessions of the long-term vulnerability, mental confusion and 'rawness' of emotions they were going through during the withdrawal syndrome. For the client it gave her the chance to talk freely and to be listened to.

Nickie had written to me about herself before she had an individual session with me. Although she was only 22 years old, she had revealed in her letter that she had been on tranquillisers for over six years. She had given birth and been divorced, her child had been made a ward of court, and she had married again and been imprisoned for a minor offence. Now she was going through withdrawal, and all her subdued emotions were just beginning to come to the surface. She was experiencing the 'volcano' effect (see pages 109–10).

As I greeted her she gave me a big smile, as if to say 'please like me.'

'How can I help you?' I asked her when she was comfortably seated.

She looked searchingly into my face as if I had all the answers. 'I don't know what's happening to me. I am so confused. I feel as if I am going mad.'

'You are not going mad. I know what you are going through, we all do at TRANX. We've all been where you are. It's all to do with withdrawal and things coming to the surface. Can you tell me how you feel?'

'I feel numb. I have no feelings.'

'You wrote in your letter that your child is in a home.'

'Yes, that's right. But I want him back. I love him. I want to give him the love my mother never gave me,' she said.

'Do you want to talk about your mother?'

'No. I can't. It hurts. I can't get the words out, they stop here.' She pointed to her throat and burst into tears.

Nickie had blocked her feelings with the drugs, like all tranquilliser addicts do. I knew, from the counselling skills I had now gained, that if I could penetrate her feelings and help her to understand them, she could then start to help herself. As the sessions progressed over the weeks, I helped to build up and find her own inner strength.

Margaret was another client who needed individual sessions. When she was off her pills she said to me: 'I got through because you believed I could do it—even when I couldn't see it. I did actually lose sight of the end. I lost all sense of judgement. But because you believed in me, that meant a lot.'

For some, TRANX was much more than just an organisation. It became their second home, especially if they were living alone. It was a place where they felt safe and secure, where they were among people who had 'been there'. Gloria lived alone. She was a bus-ride away from TRANX, and because she had no one to look after her through her withdrawal she spent most of her days in our building. 'TRANX was the only safe place for me,' she says. 'I went there every day. I'd be up at six-thirty because I couldn't sleep, and I would sit in my chair holding my head, thinking I've got a couple of hours before I go down to TRANX. In those couple of hours I'd be saying to myself, "Please Lord, don't let me go mad, don't let me go mad." Then I'd leave my flat to go and I'd be walking down the road to the bus stop and all this was going on in my head, "You're going mental, you're going to die, you're going to do something stupid." And I'd get to the bus stop and I'd sit on the seat and things would be going on around me, and I used to think "I've got to make it to TRANX." I'd stay there all day, and I'd be fine until it was time to go home, then I'd start panicking again.'

When tranquilliser addicts first came to TRANX they were desperate, confused and lost in the maze. We supported and encouraged them through some of their darkest moments, watching them get better, little by little. Our counselling worked because we could say: 'I know how you feel' and not: 'I understand these feelings are possible.' We were the proof.

After the client had been off all mood-altering drugs for two years, we had to say good-bye. We didn't want her to get hooked on our organisation! Many clients felt, as June did when she walked out of our door for the last time, that they 'couldn't have done it without TRANX'.

Over the years we were also slowly gaining respect from some people in the medical profession. Some doctors and psychiatrists, in the UK and abroad, were approaching me for information on benzo-diazepine addiction. After all, I was seeing more of the effects of tranquillisers and withdrawal on a daily basis than they were.

From 1982 to May 1990 we dealt with over 100,000 enquiries from tranquilliser addicts, and gave thousands of clients a new life without mood-altering drugs. As demonstrated on page 152, our success rate was high. I believe that the secret of our success was that we were there to listen. Our listening ear and our experience were the only tools we had, unlike the doctor whose tool of trade is often treatment with pills. The doctor always has the comfort at the back of his mind that if his counselling fails he can fall back on drugs. At TRANX we could only rely on counselling and support. The psychiatrist Dr Mark Tattersall said in a television interview: 'TRANX (UK) is filling a gap that is not filled by anyone else, and there are certainly some people who have been helped by them, who have tried other methods [of stopping tranquilliser use] and have not succeeded elsewhere.'

Once the government funding had been spent, we survived for another three years on money from the Regional Health Authority, another public authority and the Paul Getty Trust. But then that money ran out too. We asked again for a grant but were refused. We received a letter saying 'TRANX in many ways is a victim of its own success. The Health Authorities, GPs and the general public are far more aware of the dangers of long-term tranquilliser use than at any previous time. The [Local Health] Region views as a priority the continuation of work with GPs to modify their prescribing habits.' Dr Betsy Ettore viewed this funding refusal as fairly typical of the authorities. 'As far as they are concerned, self-help is help-yourself. The self-help organisation should be self-resourcing. You don't need government resources to help you. Therefore, in their view, you don't need government funding.'

The authorities saw my work as over. But I felt it had barely begun: there were still over three million people in the UK who were addicted to benzodiazepines. Who were they going to go to for help? The Government believed that they would go to the GP. But the GP is already overstretched. Has he the time to give that 'instant help' we gave with our telephone helpline? Has he the time gently to coax a tranquilliser addict through the pains of withdrawal? Has he the time to write thousands of letters to encourage people to carry on with the coming-off programme, even though it is tough? Can he spare forty minutes with a patient who doesn't know why she feels like she does? Can he put her in touch with other addicts so that she doesn't feel alone or that she is going mad? Can he support the family who don't understand what is going on? Can he stop himself from writing out a prescription for another mood-altering drug? Does he really understand the problems of withdrawal?

I tried everything in my power to save TRANX. We made public appeals on the television and in the press for charitable donations, but they all failed to raise the money we needed—failed because the general public still do not see our dependence on tranquillisers as a problem. After all, we were prescribed them by our doctors.

On 22 June 1990 the doors of TRANX (UK) were shut. At the time of writing, they have not re-opened. I do not know when, or if, they ever will. In the meantime, I am running a private, independent service (dealing with written enquiries only). The address of this service appears at the front of the book.

PART SEVEN

CHANGING ATTITUDES

HAVE WE LEARNT
FROM OUR MISTAKES?

Have we learnt anything from the benzodiazepine saga? Has any good come out of our suffering?

As far as benzodiazepines are concerned, the medical attitude to them is changing. They are no longer hailed as a 'wonder drug', but are seen in a more unfavourable light and are becoming rather unfashionable. Some doctors may now admit openly that they are addictive, although it has taken them over twenty years to realise this.

However, the benzodiazepine story is by no means over. Scientific evidence is still being accumulated about any possible long-term damage, if any, in ex-users. And there are still millions of people hopelessly hooked on the drug around the world.

The fact that benzodiazepines have dropped in popularity does not mean that there are any fewer unhappy or anxious people sitting in doctors' waiting rooms—far from it. So if doctors aren't writing out prescriptions for benzodiazepines, what are they doing to alleviate anxiety in their patients? Unfortunately, as discussed previously, they are often still prescribing other drugs, such as Buspar (buspirone), and Zimovane (zopiclone), and in some cases beta-blockers, all of which are frequently proclaimed as non-addictive and perfectly safe. In fact, doctors are being encouraged to prescribe these drugs instead of benzodiazepines, just as benzodiazepines were earlier substituted for barbiturates.

The doctor's handbook of drugs, the *MIMS* (Monthly Index of Medical Specialities), says this about these new drugs. For a beta-blocker drug it states '. . . probably less effective than the benzodiazepines, but offers a useful alternative in view of the current concern over benzodiazepine dependence.' For Buspar, it says: '. . . is a new anxiolytic which is chemically and pharmacologically distinct from benzodiazepines. Early reports indicate that it produces less sedation, psychomotor impairment or dependence and has less abuse potential than the benzodiazepines.' Of course, if a drug produces less sedation, it is less effective and the chance of addiction becomes less too.

It is worrying that doctors are seeing these new drugs as non-addictive. Dr Davis Temple, Jr, of Bristol-Myers, USA, has said, 'Buspar is as easy to stop taking as to start.'[58] But surely it has not been on the market long enough to prove otherwise?

Beta-blockers, like the benzodiazepines in their heyday, are going through a boom in sales. 'In 1987 nearly fifteen million prescriptions were filed for beta-blockers, accounting for 23 per cent of all drugs prescribed—a figure uncannily close to that of benzodiazepines at their peak,' writes Arabella Melville.[59]

Already the evidence is beginning to show that beta-blockers may cause low blood pressure, circulatory problems, sleep disturbance, cold hands and feet, tiredness, nightmares and depression—which echo the side-effects of benzodiazepines.

Although doctors are again enthusiastically writing out prescriptions for these new drugs, I view them with more caution. I find it very hard to believe that a drug which is mood-altering cannot be addictive. And Dr Heather Ashton warns: 'The benzodiazepine saga provides a cautionary example of the dangers of the over-enthusiastic prescribing of mood-altering drugs. The market is now pregnant with a new generation of non-benzodiazepine drugs to reduce anxiety, reputedly innocent of dependence-producing properties. Doctors and patients should use them with care, remembering that any drug that gives pleasure or allays suffering, whether prescribed like benzodiazepines or freely available like alcohol and caffeine, can cause dependence.'[60]

When it comes to treating stress and anxiety, many doctors may not really have changed their prescribing habits at all—they may simply have changed the type of pill they prescribe. For the radical change that is needed, both the doctor and the patient should look not towards a pill bottle for help, but towards another human being—the counsellor. They should only use these drugs for a few days in an emergency, until counselling can be found.

Unfortunately, there is still a great dearth of counsellors. The BAC (British Association for Counselling) has 6500 members in the UK, of whom 70 per cent work as counsellors.[61] But as you have read in this book, so many tranquilliser addicts don't have access to a counsellor, and have said that had they had someone to talk to at the time, they wouldn't have needed to take pills. Today, a lot of counselling falls into the hands of the GP, but he often has neither the time nor the training to help his patients with emotional problems. I would like to see counselling taken away from the doctor, and given to a trained counsellor assigned to the surgery or working in the catchment area.

Although this may seem to the layman to be a great assistance to the overworked GP, unfortunately the doctor may see it as a threat. Many doctors can be resistant to change, and could very well resent a counsellor taking over part of their work. 'Doctors often feel threatened by the thought of sharing knowledge. Their monopoly of knowledge maintains the awe in which patients hold them, and mystique is fundamental to their professional status,' write Arabella Melville and Colin Johnson.[62]

The mystique of medical knowledge carries on into the labelling of drugs. Today, in the United Kingdom, there are no warnings on a benzodiazepine bottle that it is dependence-forming with long-term use. Instead, the pharmaceutical industry relies on the doctor to impart this knowledge to his patient, either verbally or with a leaflet. But advice can be forgotten and leaflets can be lost. When the Royal Pharmaceutical Society recommended in 1988 that label warnings should be placed on all dispensed prescriptions for benzodiazepines, it was firmly out-voted. 'One delegate thought that raising doubt in the patient's mind at the time of prescribing would undermine his or her confidence in the doctor.' But Dr Peter Tyrer suggested that 'labelling would help patients to distinguish between benzodiazepines and other psychotropic [mood-altering] medication.'[63] I would like to see printed on the bottle the fact that benzodiazepines may cause dependence after just a few weeks. Then if the patient wants to carry on taking the drug for a longer period, it's by choice.

Today, we are still counting the cost of benzodiazepines in terms of suffering and loss. Millions of people are still hooked on the drug, and millions have a sad tale to tell. But the blame cannot be put on any one particular group: we are all responsible—the pharmaceutical industry, the medical profession and society—for the benzodiazepine tragedy.

Whatever we have learnt from this painful saga won't be apparent today, but may come to light in another decade or two. Let us hope that we won't then have to tell the same story about yet another mood-altering drug.

APPENDIX

BENZODIAZEPINE DATA

(as at March 1991)

Chemical/generic name	Brand name	Equivalent to 5mg Valium	Half-life*	Length of action	Anxiolytic/hypnotic
alprazolam	Xanax	0.25mg	6–12 hours	medium	A
bromazepam	Lexotan	6.00mg	10–20 hours	medium	A
chlordiazepoxide	Librium Limbitrol† Tropium	10.00mg	5–30 hours (active metabolite‡ 36–200 hours)	long	A
clobazam	Frisium	5.00mg	12–60 hours	long	A
clonazepam	Rivotril	anti-epileptic only			A
clorazepate	Tranxene	2.50mg	36–200 hours	long	A
diazepam	Alupram Atensine Diazemuls§ Solis Stesolid Tensium Valium	5.00mg	20–100 hours (active metabolite‡ 36–200 hours)	long	A
flunitrazepam	Rohypnol	0.5mg	20–30 hours (active metabolite‡ 36–200 hours)	long	H

flurazepam	Dalmane	15.00mg	20–30 hours (active metabolite‡ 40–250 hours)	long	H
loprazolam	Dormonoct	0.5mg	6–12 hours	medium	H
lorazepam	Almazine Ativan	0.5mg	10–20 hours	medium	A
lormetazepam		0.5mg	10–12 hours	medium	H
medazepam	Nobrium	4.00mg	36–200 hours (active metabolite‡)	long	A
midazolam	Hypnovel		intravenous		
nitrazepam	Mogadon Nitrados Remnos Somnite Unisomnia	5.00mg	15–38 hours	long	H
oxazepam	Oxanid	10.00mg	4–15 hours	short	A
temazepam	Normison	10.00mg	8–22 hours	medium	H
triazolam	Halcion	0.25mg	2 hours	short	H

★ The half-life of a drug is the length of time the body takes to get rid of half a dose, regardless of the size of the dose.
† Limbitrol contains Librium and Amitriptyline.
‡ 'Active metabolite' means that when the drug is digested a slightly different substance is produced.
§ Diazemuls is given as a 'pre-med'.

REFERENCES

INTRODUCTION

1 'Princeton study, 1958–60'. *Journal of the American Medical Association*, 1960, Vol. 174, p.1242

2 Celia Haddon, *Women and Tranquillisers* (Sheldon Press)

3 Drs I. H. Ingram and Gerald C. Timbury, letter to the Editor, 'Side-effects of Librium', *The Lancet*, 1 October 1960; Allen A. Bartholomew MB, 'A Dramatic Side-effect of a New Drug, "Librium"', *Medical Journal of Australia*, 9 September 1961, pp.436–7; Leslie A. Guile MB, 'Rapid Habituation to Chlordiazepoxide ("Librium")', *Medical Journal of Australia*, 13 July 1968, pp.56–7; Forensic Medicine Conference, *British Medical Journal*, 27 April 1963; Carl F. Essig MD, 'Newer Sedative Drugs That Can Cause States of Intoxication and Dependence of Barbiturate Type', *JAMA*, 23 My 1966, Vol. 196, No. 8, pp.714–17; Dr M. M. Glatt, 'Benzodiazepines', *British Medical Journal*, 13 May 1967, p.444

4 Briefing document issued at a presentation to the authors at Roche Products Ltd, Welwyn Garden City, 5 January 1990

5 Dr Heather Ashton, 'Anything for a quiet life', *New Scientist*, 6 May 1989

6 Professor Malcolm Lader, 'Anxiolytic drugs', *British Journal of Hospital Medicine*, January 1973

7 Dr John Marks, *Benzodiazepine—Use, Overuse, Misuse, Abuse* (MTP Press)

8 Dr John Marks, *Benzodiazepine—Use, Overuse, Misuse, Abuse* (MTP Press)

9 Committee on Review of Medicines, *British Medical Journal*, 29 March 1980

10 Professor Malcolm Lader, 'Withdrawal from long-term benzodiazepine treatment', *British Medical Journal*, 5 September 1981, Vol. 283, p.643

11 Roche briefing document

PART ONE

12 Dr R. H. Rahe, in *Stressful Life Events*, ed. B. S. Dohrenwend and B. P. Dohrenwend (Wiley)

13 From a workshop with Professor Malcolm Lader

14 Dr Vernon Coleman, *Life Without Tranquillisers* (Corgi)

15 Association of Community Health Councils in England and Wales, *Benzodiazepines—a Suitable Case for Treatment*, June 1989

16 Association of Community Health Councils in England and Wales, *Benzodiazepines—a Suitable Case for Treatment*, June 1989

17 Diane Wyndham, 'My doctor gives me pills to put him out of my misery: Women and psychotropic drugs', *New Doctor*, March 1982, no. 23, pp.21–5. (*New Doctor* is the journal of the Doctor's Reform Society of Australia.)

18 Letter from Virginia Bottomley, Secretary of State for Health

19 E. K. Rodrigo, M. B. King and P. Williams, 'Health of long-term benzodiazepine users', *British Medical Journal*, February 1988, Vol. 296, p.603

20 Dr Hunt, *Tranquilliser Prescribing by GPs in Brighton* (Health Studies Unit, Centre for Medical Research, University of Sussex)

21 Susie Haxthausen, World Health Organisation symposium

PART TWO

22 Dr C. Hallstrom, 'Benzodiazepine, the Medical View', SCODA (Standing Conference on Drug Addiction) newsletter, September–October 1989

23 Dr Peter Tyrer, 'The risk of dependence on benzodiazepine drugs: the importance of patient selection', *British Medical Journal*, 14 January 1989, Vol. 298, pp.102–5

24 'Second Opinion', *The Independent*, 28 January 1990

25 From an interview with Dr Heather Ashton

26 Dr Heather Ashton, 'Benzodiazepines—the present position', *The Darlington Postgraduate*, January 1990

27 Dr Heather Ashton, 'Benzodiazepines—the present position', *The Darlington Postgraduate*, January 1990

28 Dr Heather Ashton, 'Anything for a quiet life', *New Scientist*, 6 May 1989

29 *Observer*, March 1988

30 Allen A. Bartholomew MB, 'A dramatic side-effect of a new drug, "Librium"', *Medical Journal of Australia*, 1961, p.473

31 Professor R. G. Priest, 'Benzodiazepine and dependence', *Bulletin of the Royal College of Psychiatrists*, Vol. 12, p.88

32 Dr Vernon Coleman, *Life Without Tranquillisers* (Corgi)

33 From a workshop with Dr Peter Tyrer

34 Dr Heather Ashton, *Protracted Withdrawal Syndromes from Benzodiazepines* (Newcastle University)

35 From an interview with Dr Heather Ashton

36 Dr Heather Ashton, 'Benzodiazepines—the present position', *The Darlington Postgraduate*, January 1990

37 From an interview with Dr Heather Ashton

38 Dr Vernon Coleman

39 Shirley Trickett, *Coming Off Tranquillisers and Sleeping Pills* (Thorsons Publishing Group)

40 Shirley Trickett, *Coming Off Tranquillisers and Sleeping Pills* (Thorsons Publishing Group)

41 Dr Heather Ashton, 'Benzodiazepines withdrawal: an unfinished story', *British Medical Journal*, 14 August 1984, Vol. 288

PART THREE

42 Drs R. Noyes, M. J. Garvey, B. L. Cook and P. J. Perry, 'Benzodiazepine withdrawal: a review of the evidence', *Journal of Clinical Psychiatry*, 10 October 1988, Vol. 49

43 From an interview with Dr Heather Ashton

44 Dr Heather Ashton, 'Risk of dependence on benzodiazepine drugs: a major problem of long-term treatment', *British Medical Journal*, 14 January 1989, Vol. 298

45 Drs A. C. Higgitt, M. H. Lader and P. Fonagy, 'Clinical management of benzodiazepine dependence', *British Medical Journal*, 14 September 1985, Vol. 291

PART FOUR

46 Dr Heather Ashton, 'Anything for a quiet life', *New Scientist*, 6 May 1989

47 Dr D. M. Davies, *Textbook of Adverse Drug Reactions* (Oxford University Press, 1981)

48 Dr L. Olegard, 'Teratogenic effect of benzodiazepines during pregnancy', *Journal of Paediatrics*, January 1989, p.126

49 Arabella Melville and Colin Johnson, *Cured to Death* (New English Library)

50 Dr Heather Ashton, 'Anything for a quiet life', *New Scientist*, 6 May 1989

51 Arabella Melville and Colin Johnson, *Cured to Death* (New English Library)

PART FIVE

52 Dr Heather Ashton , 'Benzodiazepine withdrawal in 50 patients', *British Journal of Addiction*, 1987, Vol. 82, pp.665–71

53 From an interview with Dr Heather Ashton

54 Dr Edmonson and Helen King, *Women Talking* (in association with the Addiction Research Unit, Institute of Psychiatry, University of London)

55 Drs J. Catalan, D.H. Gath, 'Benzodiazepines in general practice: time for a decision', *British Medical Journal*, 11 May 1985, Vol. 290

56 Jane Madders, *Stress and Relaxation* (Martin Dunitz)

57 Professor Malcolm Lader, at an educational media workshop sponsored by Bristol-Myers: 'Anxiety management: a closer look at the facts', 11 January 1990

PART SEVEN

58 From an educational media workshop sponsored by Bristol-Myers: 'Anxiety management: a closer look at the facts', 11 January 1990

59 Arabella Melville, 'The new tranquilliser trap', *Vogue*, October 1989

60 Dr Heather Ashton, 'Anything for a quite life', *New Scientist*, 6 May 1989

61 Figures from the British Association for Counselling

62 Arabella Melville and Colin Johnson, *Cured to Death* (New English Library)

63 Dr Peter Tyrer, *Lancet*, 12 November 1988, p.1153

INDEX